LANGUAGES OF WATER

EDITED BY
EUGEN BACON

MVmedia, LLC
Fayetteville, GA

MVmedia, LLC
PO Box 14325
Fayetteville, GA 30214
www.mvmediaatl.com

Book Layout ©2017 BookDesignTemplates.com
Cover Design by Uraeus
Cover Art by John Jennings

Ordering Information:
Quantity sales. Special discounts are available on quantity purchases by corporations, associations, and others. For details, contact the "Special Sales Department" at the address above.

Languages of Water/ Eugen Bacon, ed. -- 1st ed.
ISBN 979-8-9857336-6-2

Contents

To all who thirst

Yet as eons pass in one beat of the heart, you hear the rustle under the trees. Taste the bite of death.

–'EVRIDIKI', DOMINIQUE HECQ

Dedication

To
WrICE & Singlit Station

~~~

Languages of Water is a rare but intimate fusion of East, West and Africa, a stunning artefact of writerly immersion and cultural exchange. This child of digital collaboration brings together writers, illustrators and translators of poetry, fiction and essays, and refuses to be contained.

In a playful interrogation of French literary theorist, critic and philosopher Roland Barthes' *le plaisir du texte* and death of the author, *Languages of Water* opens with the homing story 'When the Water Stops'. Cross-cultural creators interpret the story in different forms of itself, offering subversive fiction, poetry, essays, monochrome graphics and sudden fiction, and translations of the homing story in English, Swahili, French, Cantonese, Malay, Vietnamese and Bengali.

The concept of this cross-lingual hybrid is birthed from the Writers Immersion and Cultural Exchange (WrICE), founded by members of non/fictionLab at RMIT University. At the heart of WrICE is a simple idea: to give writers of different backgrounds a chance to step outside familiar writing practices and contexts and connect deeply with writers from different cultures and across generations in an immersive residency. The respectful and generative space for
~~~

reflection, conversation, creative sharing and surprise that WrICE offers affords writers a muse—a precious opportunity to explore possibilities outside comfort zones and borrow something new into own creative practice. It sparks connections and grows a cohesive community of writers that spans boundaries.

In October 2021 WrICE brought together 12 writers and translators of poetry, fiction and non-fiction from Singapore, Sri Lanka, Myanmar, Vietnam, Hong Kong, the Philippines, Japan and Australia in a three-week digital residency.

Together with WrICE 2021 fellows, including award-winning novelist, memoirist, and essayist Francesca Rendle-Short, *Languages of Water* offers work by acclaimed authors—award-winning writer of Scottish and English heritage David Carlin; Korean essayist and translator Kyong-mi Park; 'Queen of African Horror' Nuzo Onoh; renowned slipstream writer Andrew Hook; widely-published scholar in international journals and anthologies Oz Hardwick; bilingual and award-winning Seb Doubinsky; newly awarded James Currey Fellow for African literature Stephen Embleton; award-winning Belgian poet and translator who writes across genres and tongues Dominique Hecq; and specially invited contributors.

To Write Water

Francesca Rendle-Short and David Carlin

splash *splish* wading through *thermometers of snow*
rivulets *trickles* gulp *and when it goes down*

It starts very slow with a drip.
Drip. Drip.
Drip.
And salt.

That's the first thing. An invitation to write water.

Then this: slam poet and Djapu writer from Yirrkala in East Arnhem Land Melanie Mununggurr brings with her the skins of saltwater people, memories soaked in water, where the water remembers. She takes us to the reeds, the rocks, and rivers, takes us to the edge of intricacies of water-knows, gives us colours of the earth, gives us bloodlines and pain—so much pain—asks the whys of beats and bruises and resistance in ashes, in salt, in sand.

She tells us again, again the water will remember all.

Drip.
Drip.
Drip.

Water, memory, and I think of sprinklers, making fanning circles on the hoped-for lawns of half-parched Perth, bore water sucked up from underground as if it came from a reservoir big as the universe. A tractor sprinkler, which was a sprinkler that could drive itself along a hose. If you were fancy and could afford it, you would put in reticulation and the water would flow underground in pipes and pop up at regular intervals. The water of a brief time of magical thinking. Oasis thinking, settler thinking.

Stories drip, word by word and sentence by sentence, from mouth to mouth, in a game of pass the parcel, unwrapping and passing along the chain from pool to pool (my metaphors are mixing up like goo).

~~~

the wrong way percussive drip drip *a neighbour's gutter* The Great Ocean Road *never seen a* bite

Can we really do this?

The water, the drink of it, the float and swell, full immersion.

Because here there is a speculatively pitched register of fire and storm when the water stops in a deep languorous cadence, tongue curled around vowels, syllables and syntax, glucose and convulsion, ashes floating in air, awash, swirling—figuratively speaking—to bring this bleed into existence. And breath. Not breath. The giving of this thing to our collective imaginaries with hands trickling through fingers the bonds of atom
~~~

and molecule and compound. The science of water, poesis. Chemistry. Making things happen (that didn't exist before). It sizzles. It hisses, it curls.

Water, futures, and once not too long ago our government spent a vast amount of money building a desalination plant, in those seasons when the long drought came. Since then, it has gone into mothballs because there have been years of floods instead. They built it, they said, to *future-proof*, as if that was all that it would take. What kind of future are we proofing for, and against?

Poems ooze, but actually I don't know that for sure, I've never tidied up after any. For all I know poems evaporate, beginning in a vast sea of words from which all but a very few are disappeared, and those left behind float in clumps, salty or sweet, condensing on the tongue.

Water, present, the other day it rained so hard (because our city has moved towards the tropics now) that the water came in under all the gaps beneath the doors in our weatherboard house and drenched the surfaces through every window it found open. Puddling.

Find a puddle and a small child and pretty soon the small child will be walking in the puddle, because—just because. Because why wouldn't you go walking through a puddle if you were lucky enough to come upon one. What is funnier than a puddle? Nothing is funnier than a puddle, only made funnier still by gumboots.

~~~

whale bottom feeders *the nibbling tank* sound of sonics *at night the waves are louder* smell of *oo*

I notice/noticed water.
Because.
I am a water person.
Water is something to love in past and present tense.
I taught myself to swim.
Blood lines. Water lines. Water words.
Handwriting like water, someone else says.
(*I loved but never knew how to do it.*)
Swimming gives perspective.
Water in person. Here.

Let's write our way to the sea. And beyond.
Water as carrier of words. Water as solvent. Let's sketch our way into this. Word by word we go to the rim of sea hand in hand where we go in, we go out far, we go deep, we go wild; where nothing else matters. Inside water. Here it is all language and grammar and preposition under water behind cloud above wing towards wave inside swell, the mathematics of sea water—the making of sign with hands, and patterns and equations. The floating of love and language in/and of warm pockets, the body swimming like a boat, bubbles and weightlessness. It is love and the arrangement or speaking of commitment: finding a syntax to fit, seamless, into the one sentence, the
~~~

sound of familial geometry. It is drowning and not drowning. Dreaming and floating. Seagrasses and gropers and sea dragons.

The luckiest thing is to float down a river, have the current take you away until you catch yourself sometime later somewhere quite different, or at least around the bend.

The luckiest thing is to float on your back in the ocean, pushing out your chest so the water falls off and you are just there, a starfish under the hot sun.

~~~

salt water *frozen toes* d r i n k *parched* diluted solutions *sweat and* fizzle and slop *and gush* leak

Someone says: in Vietnamese the word water *nước* is the same word for country. It is not a coincidence. The full form of the word *country* is *đất nước* where *đất* is for earth and soil, the ground or land, and *nước* is for water. Which brings us to wet rice, the growing of staples amongst other material things, and acknowledgement.

In Chinese when you drink water 飲水思源 'remember the source'.

(*How strangely the same tongue sits in different mouths.*)
~~~

Remember where you come from, your origin. A want. Something missing. The source.

Acknowledge Sea Country across and around Australia.

Acknowledge the traditional custodians of country throughout Australia and recognise their continuing connection to land, waters, and community.

Acknowledge writing/swimming on land and sea that has never been ceded.

Pay respects to Elders past and present. Now. Here.

Fish swim in schools around your knees, and why is it that these are schools, what is it that the fish are learning?

What happens if writers swim in schools? What happens if writers hide out under rock shelfs, submerged together, gathering their strength as the tide changes, the ocean breathes slowly in and out? What happens if writers splash and persist in splashing even when the voice on the loudspeaker asks them to quieten down, as if they might cause the concrete that holds the pool in to collapse, as if they might stain the nice clean tiles with their unmentionable liquids? What happens if they start to pretend that ice is steam, and steam is water, and the kettle is boiling loudly, and the bath is overflowing and the hose has a leak and everything has flown away, like flowing was the same as flying?

~~~

—*filled bruises* urinating *buckets!* holes in the roof letting through *clouds of* atmospheres, *joyous*

Drip.

What if?

She harvests salt water and makes salt crystals. It takes a long time.

We drip after. We drip intermezzo. Mezzo. Drip and know we are alive. Drip and know we are not dead. Not yet.

To write water is to write from watery flesh, harbingers and auguries in solution, colandered dreams, whispers of old waterfalls, dry salt lakes of tears, ice pressed into the shape of pineapples, drive-in cinemas in which hail obscures the screen and thrums so loud on the roof you could scream at the top of your lungs and nobody would hear you; to write water is also to sip and quench and splutter; to pool it in your hands.
~~~

Postscript

Thank you to all the WrICE writers and translators who took part in WrICE 2021 who shared their writing and their thinking; who swam together across the two weeks: Eugen Bacon, John Bengan, Cheng Tim Tim, Audrey Chin, Clara Chow, Rina Kikuchi, Ramya Jirasinghe, Melanie Mununggurr, Quyên Nguyễn-Hoàng, Pandora, Alvin Pang, Francesca Rendle-Short.

Salt and Survival by Melanie Mununggurr, written and performed by Melanie Mununggurr, music by Beatrice Lewis, ABC Classics, 2020, <https://www.face-
book.com/watch/?v=1134879057427085>

When the Water Stops

Eugen Bacon

As the climate turned, it hurled at them bush-fires that razed huts to the ground, dust storms that swept away families, drought—all the cattle and sheep gone, reduced to skin, then skeletons. At first, the villagers took turns on the bleed, sharing dreams and fears, understanding that as a people they were the same.

But a typical grown male has a blood volume of just five litres—a forty per cent loss is deadly. The threshold thirty-nine per cent has only ninety-two per cent water in it; the rest is washed away in glucose, hormones, proteins, fats, vitamins, mineral salts and carbon dioxide—what good is it? $C0_2$ may induce dizziness, tiredness, restlessness, convulsions or coma. So, given all the minuses, how much water would be left from a bleed to go around a village?

They sifted the question in their minds while volunteers, having bled for the clan, sucked on cactus leaves and sap, figs and desert ants for four to eight weeks afterward. But still they were not strong enough to take another turn when it arrived. The loss was not replenished.

So where first they volunteered, now they drew sticks—it was plain luck, or missed luck. A stick was a stick, a short one was short. If you drew it, your fate was sealed, your only solace that this death would not be a lonely one, but rather a communion that met society's needs.

But even the drawing of sticks stopped eventually. It was a sacrifice too big. So now it was a matter for those with money, or bigger sticks, to determine who to massacre.

And that determined whose ashes would float in the air, figuratively speaking. What really happened took place in the vat.

The woman in the vat

What she's doing this week is sitting in a bowl, right there in the heat shimmer. She's awash with memories of drowsing, unfolding, everything in slow motion. When she looks back on this time, what will she remember? She watches the smoke swirling like a benevolent hug, giant clouds bubbling out the words: *Where are you now?* Her soul is an object brightest in the sky. Today, she's a bleed. Tomorrow is a wish.

The leader of the nation

Ten years ago, the big leader came out of his shelter, determined to occupy the steps of a shrine opened as a museum to the Pope. He stunned human rights leaders, a few high courts and many mothers when he pushed out his lip and held up a Bible for one full minute as cameras snapped. Riot police fell with batons, rubber bullets and gas masks on peaceful protesters brandishing slogans about the art of cherishing and love.

What was a drop of blood when the economy outweighed civil unrest and stocks soared higher? Did you see the Dow, a gain of 267 points? And the advances in the Nasdaq Composite?

Evolutionary theory was all about natural selection of the form that would leave the most copies of itself.

Light-years on, every archbishop in an alternate universe, outraged by the misuse of a facility of worship, would consider the historic violation of the principles of humanity and utter three spaced words: I. Can't. Breathe.

Protests were always ugly, thought the leader. And a new election was coming up.

The rich woman in the metropolis

When the water stops, the blood must flow, says the woman with a rainbow diamond shaped into a bangle around her wrist. The billion-dollar brooch—a set with an aurora pendant—was a gift from a cousin of a cousin of a great-uncle whose name she tried to remember but couldn't. It was just too hard.

She flourishes from the catastrophe of others. Blooms on the unimportant. Like the people in her cellar, beggars from the village. Theirs is a narrative she doesn't believe in, the kind of story reflected in old photos by art historians. Her fabric is the politics that gave rise to Hitler, Mussolini and Idi Amin Dada. She can't help it if those people don't belong in a near-perfect picture. They are mistakes, awkward memories that float a different image every time she looks, never authentic. There are many books about humanity, but this is hard!

Turn off the sound of their groaning! she snaps to her servants. The moaning is a sound that's never black or white. It doesn't obey the rules of composition. If their cry is a question, it's a cry in a language of Babel. She doesn't understand its vowels, syllables, syntax, parables or context, and it's impossible to try. Because that's so hard!

What's not hard to understand is vintage produce with a good nose. The ones from the village come at a good price and their blood is pure, uncontaminated by the city's pollution. Village blood combines the right acidity with a sweet aroma of smoke. Bacon and pepper, violets inside a copper finish.

And vintage blood must flow for the survival of her species. She cradles with affection a labradoodle puppy to her breast.

A village husband under pressure

The revolution came when he alluded to reason.

It was a reason created from the reflection of fourteen hungry mouths and three dry cassava biscuits to go around. It was a reason that made him ask the question: wife or children? She'd brought them into existence. They initiated a cycle of living that was a torment.

Perhaps his was an excuse to be unkind, to give voice to everyday hatreds, resentments, regrets . . . They crept in like dwarf monkeys and grew into pests: stealing, raiding, and all that. He was not the sort of person to hold a grudge on matters that came along with a sad marriage, so it was right to say it was fear that decided his choice. When his wife's own revolution came, there was no question where her truth lay: husband or children?

He made things happen, yeah. Sorry. They said what happened in a vat was quick.

He did miss having someone to rant to. But there was enough money to feed hungry children now, the youngest just two. Afia, the Friday-born child. Abimbola, the rich-born child but always poor. Amara, the graceful one now potbellied and bald with kwashiorkor. Chi, Ke, Re, Po, the quadruplets with nylon hair and eyes filled with sand.

He made things happen because, after the wife . . . Fourteen options still.

Afia, fifth of fourteen motherless ones

I am a broken egg on a blistered road. A dying bird on a razor-wire fence. The jackal trots this way, that way, sizing up how to eat me. My nostalgia is here again, no school, no soup. Just an empty sky whistling as we bury our dead. I am a marked card—red marks the spot. The arrow will whiz into the eye of a dried-up fountain. Are you my mother? There's a skeleton trapped in the black mamba's hissing. Grey feathers swirling the wrong way.

The youngest child speaks

I'm in search of something I don't know. There's a hand and a gaze, a smile and a scent. It's a comfort, it's a warmth. I don't remember the face that comes and goes, the love that is a crack. It's complicated, it's unsafe. Blurred and full of crumble.

Nostalgia, a great-uncle with empty sacks, an odour of mothballs in his breath, his eyes a fortress against hope. You think of this moment, over and over, wishing you and the rest of the world remembered different.

Quand l'eau se tarit

Dominique Hecq

(French translation of 'When the Water Stops')

Lorsque le climat changea, celui-ci fit flamber des feux de brousse qui décimèrent leurs huttes, précipita des tempêtes de poussière qui emportèrent des familles entières, balaya leurs terres d'une sécheresse – tous leurs bestiaux, tous leurs moutons disparus, la peau sur les os, puis de vrais squelettes. Au début, les villageois se relayèrent pour la saignée, échangeant rêves et inquiétudes, convaincus qu'en tant que peuple ils étaient tous semblables.

En revanche, on sait qu'à peine cinq litres de sang ne circulent dans le corps d'un homme adulte – une perte sanguine de quarante pour cent est fatale. La valeur seuil fixée à trente-neuf pour cent ne prend en compte que quatre-vingt-deux pour cent de liquide ; le reste emporte glucose, hormones, protéines, lipides, vitamines, minéraux et dioxyde de carbone – à quoi tout cela rime-t-il ? le CO_2 peut provoquer des vertiges, une grande fatigue, de l'agitation, des convulsions et même le coma. Alors, étant-donné tous ces inconvénients, quelle quantité d'eau peut-on estimer gaspillée au terme d'une saignée au village ?

Ils retournèrent la question dans leur tête pendant que les volontaires qui avaient donné leur sang pour le clan suçaient des feuilles de cactus juteuses, des figues et des fourmis du désert durant quatre à huit semaines après la saignée. Malgré cela ils n'étaient pas prêts à supporter un nouvel événement climatique hors du commun lorsqu'il se produit. La perte du précieux liquide n'avait pas été renflouée.

Alors qu'au début ils s'étaient portés volontaire, à présent ils tiraient à la courte paille – la chance leur souriait ou pas. Une paille était une paille, une courte paille était courte. Si on la tirait, destin scellé ; la seule consolation dans la mort était que celle-ci ne serait pas une chose lente et inutile, mais une sorte de communion sociale régie par des lois tribales.

Toutefois, le moment arriva quand même tirer à la courte paille cessa. Le sacrifice était trop grand. Il revint alors aux riches, ou à ceux qui possédaient les plus longues pailles, de déterminer qui massacrer.

Certes, cela déterminait aussi ceux dont les cendres allaient flotter dans l'air, au sens figuré, bien sûr. Ce qui advint réellement se déroula dans la cuve.

La femme dans la cuve

Ce qu'elle fait cette semaine, c'est languir, le cul dans une bassine avec la chaleur qui poudroie. Elle est inondée de souvenirs d'une certaine somnolence, d'une certaine plénitude – tout au ralenti. Quand elle se remémorera cette période de sa vie, de quoi se souviendra-t-elle ? Elle regarde la fumée tourbillonner comme la promesse d'une étreinte ; de géants nuages bouillonnants éclatent de mots : *Mais où es-tu* ? Son âme est un objet étincelant dans le ciel. Aujourd'hui, elle est une saignée. Demain est un vœu.

L'élu de la nation

Il y a dix ans, l'élu notable sortit de son refuge, décidé à occuper les marches face au mausolée – aussi un musée – construit en l'honneur du Pape. Il stupéfia les leaders des droits de l'homme, quelques tribunaux de grande instance et un nombre considérable de mères de famille quand il tira la langue en brandissant sa Bible une minute durant tandis que les paparazzi prenaient des photos. La police anti-émeute descendit dans la rue où des contestataires pacifiques déployaient des slogans disant l'amour et l'art de chérir son prochain. La police agita matraques et masques à gaz et tira des balles en caoutchouc.

Que signifiait une goutte de sang quand l'économie l'emportait sur l'instabilité civile et quand la valeur des actions montait en flèche ? Aviez-vous remarqué que le Dow Jones avait grimpé de 267 cotes ? Et l'avancée de Nasdaq ? La théorie de l'évolution prenait strictement en compte la sélection naturelle – c'est à dire l'aptitude à léguer le plus grand nombre de copies d'une espèce particulière.

Des années lumières plus tard, les archevêques de certains univers parallèles, indignés par l'utilisation abusive d'un lieu de culte, seraient amenés à considérer la violation historique des conventions relatives aux droits de l'homme et prononceraient cinq mots espacés : Je. Ne. Peux. Pas. Respirer.

Les manifestations sont toujours dégueulasses, se dit l'élu. Certes, une élection s'annonçait.

La richissime femme de la métropole

Quand l'eau se tarit, le sang doit couler, dit la femme au diamant arc-en-ciel en forme de bracelet qui lui enserre le poignet. La broche, un billion de dollars – une parure avec pendentif aurore – le cadeau d'un cousin d'un cousin d'un grand-oncle dont elle essayait de se remémorer le nom, mais en vain. C'était simplement trop dur.

Elle prospère des malheurs des autres. S'enrichit d'insignifiance. Tout comme les gens enfermés dans sa cave à vin : les mendiants du village. Leurs récits sont des histoires auxquelles elle ne croit pas – elles ont le reflet terni de photos qui pullulent en histoire de l'art. Elle est faite de fibres politiques qui ont engendré Hitler, Mussolini et Idi Amin Dada. Elle n'en peut rien si ces gens ne sont pas à l'image d'une approximation de la perfection. Ce sont des erreurs, de gênants souvenirs qui projettent des images autres à chaque fois que son regard erre – jamais authentiques. Il existe nombre de livres sur l'humanité, mais ça c'est dur !

Faites taire leurs gémissements ! glapit-elle à ses serviteurs. Implorer n'est jamais noir ou blanc. Ça n'obéit pas aux règles de composition. Si le cri du cœur est une question, c'est un cri dans la langue de Babel. Elle ne comprend ni ses voyelles, syllabes, paraboles, ni sa syntaxe, ni son contexte, et il lui est impossible de s'y essayer. Parce que c'est tellement dur !

Ce qui n'est pas dur à concevoir, ce sont les vins provenant d'un cru célèbre au bouquet divin.

Ceux du village ne sont pas chers et leur sang est pur, non corrompu par la pollution de la ville. Le sang du village harmonise une impeccable acidité et un très fin arome de fumée. Bacon et poivre, violettes, palais subtilement cuivré.

Et il se doit que le sang millésime coule pour la survie de son espèce. Elle serre avec affection son petit labradoodle sur son sein.

Un mari du village stressé

La révolution surgit lorsqu'il fit allusion à la raison.

Cette raison lui était apparue alors qu'il réfléchissait aux trois biscuits de manioc destinés à quatorze bouches affamées. C'était une raison qui le poussait à *poser la question : femme ou enfants ? Elle leur avait donné la vie. Leur* existence avait initié un cycle de tourment. Peut-être était-ce là une excuse pour se montrer cruel, exprimer ses rages quotidiennes, ses rancœurs, ses doléances… Celles-ci s'étaient coulées dans sa tête comme des marmosets, puis elles sont devenues des parasites : vols, raids et tout ce qui s'en suit. Il n'était pas du genre rancunier en matière de ce qui accompagne un triste mariage, aussi peut-on dire que c'est la peur qui détermina son choix. Certes, quand le mouvement de révolte de sa femme s'était manifesté, la question du mari ou des enfants ne s'était pas posée.

Il s'activa, oh que oui ! Désolé. On dit que ce qui échut dans la cuve fut bref.

N'avoir personne à houspiller lui manquait. Mais il y avait à présent assez d'argent pour nourrir les enfants affamés – le plus jeune, tout juste deux ans. Afia, l'enfant né un vendredi. Adimbola, l'enfant né riche mais toujours sans le sou. Amara, autrefois gracile, maintenant bedonnante et chauve à cause de la kwashiorkor. Chi, Ke, Re, Po, les quadruplets aux yeux remplis de sable et cheveux de nylon.

Il s'activa parce que, après la femme... Reste quatorze options.

Afia, le cinquième de quatorze sans mère

Je suis un œuf brisé sur un chemin boursouflé. Un oiseau en train de mourir sur une clôture de barbelés. Le chacal va et vient au trot, figurant comment me manger. Ma nostalgie est de retour : pas d'école, pas de soupe. Rien, juste un ciel vide qui crisse quand nous enterrons nos cadavres. Je suis un carton marqué – le rouge marque le lieu. La flèche filera dans l'œil d'une fontaine asséchée. Etes-vous ma mère ? Il y a un squelette pris au piège dans le sifflement du mamba noir. Des plumes grises tourbillonnent dans le mauvais sens.

Le plus jeune parle.

Je cherche quelque chose mais je ne sais pas quoi. Il y a une main et un regard, un sourire et un parfum. C'est une consolation, une chaleur. Je ne me souviens pas du visage qui apparait puis disparait, de l'amour qui est une faille. C'est compliqué. C'est dangereux. Tout est brouillé et plein de ruines.

La nostalgie, un grand-oncle aux poches vides ; son haleine, une odeur de naphtaline ; ses yeux, une forteresse contre tout espoir. Vous ressassez ce moment tout en espérant vous en souvenir avec le reste du monde, autre.

New Winds

Quyên Nguyễn-Hoàng

For E.B. and N.T.H.

As the wind called *Renovation!* runs through the village
it hurls at them
bushfires
dust storms
drought
daughters
hamlets
& carpets of blackened bone
swirling in the hot hard
air.

Every day the obedient villagers take turns to bleed in a daily ritual to give thanks to the arrival of the new wind. Reforms & riches will come, will come, but first, blood will flow.

As the wind called *Renovation!* runs through the village
it hurls at them
dizziness
tiredness
restlessness
convulsions
coma
cactus spines
oozing sap
bruised figs

bones of desert ants

& ashes

ashes

ashes.

Late afternoon, while everyone is wearily waiting for the bright signs of progress, the blind village scribe sits down on the edge of the field, humming an ancient song to the darkening sky: *O the passerines have stopped singing in pairs / Whose ash is it whose ash is it floating floating in the air?*

The country belle sleeping in the bloodvat

What she is doing this morning is sitting naked in an earthen vat surrounded by red coals, her long black hair covering her back. She is waiting for her hour to bleed for the sacrifice. To merge into the gusts of the promised paradise. Drowsing, she vaguely watches the nervous smoke rising through her, swirling around her like a benevolent hug. Giant clouds before her eyes bubble out the whitish words: *Whose ash O whose ash is it floating floating in your hair?* The flight of her soul, they say, will be as bright & brief as a comet in the sky.

The leader of the nation

He holds up a Bible for one full morning as cameras snap. Meanwhile gas-masked policemen continue to hurl batons at the peaceful protesters kneeling in the streets. Protests are always so ugly, thinks the leader. Late afternoon, the blueblack protesters, still kneeling, glance up at the mist of orange gas that keeps hovering about them as it inscribes the same vile word over & over & over upon the air: UGLYUGLYUG-LYUGLY

The landlady in the capital city

She has a large jade bangle around her wrist, a gift from a cousin, a descendant of a great-uncle whose name she has never remembered. Too long, his name. Too long, like the line of village beggars waiting at her door, crying out for her Wonder Bread. *Turn off their groans!* she snaps to her servants. The moaning outside is not grammatical. She doesn't understand their noisy dialect, which irritates her. But she likes their blood, their blood tastes pure. Uncontaminated by city pollution, it has the right acidity, smells like sweet smoke. This evening, she is craving a bowl of village blood steamed with lemongrass. Lovingly she cradles her perfumed bald puppy to her white mediocre-sized breast.

Fourteen village children

Fourteen open mouths

Three dry cassava cakes to go around

Fourteen blocks of resentment & regret

Two dry cassava cakes to go around

Fourteen faces turn to the heavens where a haze of grey smoke intones an old folk tune: *O Mr. Sky Mr. Sky / Why O Why Was I Born / Why Why O Mr. Sky?*

One dry cassava cake to go around

Fourteen hungry bandits, waiting, eyes full of red dust

Asiafricalatina, fifth of fourteen loveless ones

I am a broken egg on a blistered summer road.
A dying bird on a crumbling fence.
The jackal trots this way that way,
sizing up how to eat me.

No schoolbooks no clothes no rice,
just a bowl of sorrows,
an empty bright sky
& a hundred burning suns.

They have murdered the night.
At the end of the alley someone is burying her dead. Hey?
Are you my mother? Why was I born?
The scorched bones

poking out of my flesh are starting to hiss their burned questions.
It is past the hour of sundown,

why is it still so bright?   Where has night gone?

Why is my right iris rotating the wrong way?

The youngest child speaks

I am searching for a face I don't know. There's a hand, a gaze, a smile, a scent. A comfort. A coolness. The face keeps coming & going, flickering like a silk veil in the noonlight. Lately it's hot & dry like high noon all day long. The bells are tolling among the pines in the forest, tolling for the beguiled & disappeared. I am searching for a face I don't know. An ancestor perhaps. Like the great-great-uncle who tames wild winds in my late mother's fables. But today when he pays me a visit, I see that his magical bag is emptied of cosmic wind & favorable dews. As he stands there in our thirsty pale garden, I notice a look of eternal confusion on his face, an odour of mothballs in his rueful breath. He exhales a flow of blue vapour, which floats up then condenses into a huge cloud of cries that seem to be echoing & tumbling out of the fiery suns:

I am just as befuddled as you are, son. Down there, the dead have become as desolate as the living. I am searching for a face I don't know. Are you my mother? Why is the riverbank filled with felled trees, scorched roots & the smell of burned hair? The lips of my magical bag are deciduous. Would you like to touch them?

Upon my touch, the lips of his bag along with the whole of his body immediately vanish into the blinding sunlight. A trail of hot dust lingers on my fingertips for a while, then it all quickly disperses into the raging wind that keeps running through my village. Wind and dust lash at my skin like a thousand silent knives, engraving a pattern of infinite bewilderment upon my raw, raw skin.

Gió Mới

Quyên Nguyễn-Hoàng

(Vietnamese version of 'New Winds')

Gửi E.B. and N.T.H

Làn gió mang tên *Đổi Mới!* thổi qua làng
và ném về phía họ
rừng cháy
bão bụi
        hạn hán
                những bé gái
                        xóm làng
& thảm dài những mảnh xương đen
                xoay tròn trong bầu khí đanh
            nóng

Hàng ngày, dân làng thay nhau dâng máu làm lễ tạ ơn, họ tạ ơn hiện diện của gió mới. Cải cách & giàu sang sẽ đến, sẽ đến, nhưng trước hết, máu sẽ chảy.

Làn gió mang tên *Đổi Mới!* thổi qua làng
và ném về phía họ
chóng mày chóng mặt
mỏi mệt
        bồn chồn
                co cứng
hôn mê
gai xương rồng
        nhựa cây ứa chảy
                những quả sung bầm

xương của đàn kiến

sa mạc

& tro

tro

tro.

Chiều muộn, trong khi tất cả đang uể oải chờ đợi dấu sáng của tiến bộ thì người chép sử làng, một người đàn ông mù, ngồi xuống bên mép cánh đồng, và ngân nga một bài ca cũ, ngân nga cho bầu trời tối dần cùng nghe: *Ôi lũ sẻ đã ngưng hót từng đôi / Còn lại tro ai, tro ai bềnh bồng giữa thinh không?*

Nàng hoa khôi làng say ngủ trong bể máu

Sáng nay, nhiệm vụ của nàng là ngồi mình trần trong bể chứa có than hồng bao quanh, mái tóc đen của nàng trải dài kín lưng. Nàng ngồi đợi đến lượt mình chảy máu cho lễ tế. Để hòa mình vào cơn gió thổi từ thiên đường tương lai. Nàng mơ ngủ nhìn làn khói dâng xuyên qua cơ thể nàng, cuộn xoáy quanh nàng, rộng lượng ôm lấy nàng. Một đám mây khổng lồ ùa vào mắt nàng những dòng chữ trắng mờ: *Còn lại tro ai, tro ai bềnh bồng trong tóc ngươi*? Người ta nói, hồn nàng sẽ bay sáng ngời & ngắn ngủi như đuôi sao chổi ngang qua vòm trời.

Nhà lãnh đạo quốc gia

Ông cầm cuốn Kinh suốt sáng cho máy quay ghi hình. Còn cảnh sát đeo mặt nạ chống độc thì

tiếp tục dội dùi cui vào những người biểu tình ôn hòa đang quỳ dọc con phố. Biểu tình bao giờ cũng khó coi, nhà lãnh đạo nghĩ. Chiều muộn, những người biểu tình xanh bầm vẫn quỳ yên đó, họ ngước nhìn luồng khí đang cuộn xoáy trên trời, một đám sương lầm rầm phát ra chuỗi âm dài màu da cam:
KHÓCOIKHÓCOIKHÓCOIKHÓCOI

Bà địa chủ ở kinh thành
Quanh cổ tay bà là chiếc vòng ngọc lớn, quà từ người em họ xa, con cháu của một ông chú cụ kị mà bà chưa bao giờ nhớ tên. Tên lão quá dài. Dài như hàng người ăn xin từ ngôi làng cứ lũ lượt kéo về đây, đợi chờ trước cổng nhà bà, kêu khóc van xin cho được một ổ Bánh Mì Kỳ Diệu. *Tắt tiếng rên của bọn nó đi!* bà gắt với kẻ hầu. Tiếng rên ngoài kia không đúng ngữ pháp. Bà không hiểu phương ngữ ầm ĩ của lũ này, bà khó chịu. Nhưng bà thích máu của chúng, máu chúng có vị tinh khiết, không bị ô uế do ô nhiễm thành thị. Máu chúng có độ chua vừa phải, có mùi khói ngòn ngọt. Tối nay bà thèm một bát máu làng hấp xả. Bà âu yếm ôm chú chó con hói đầu thơm nức vào ngực bà, một bộ ngực trắng cỡ trung bình.

Mười bốn đứa trẻ làng

Mười bốn khuôn miệng mở

& ba miếng sắn khô

Mười bốn khối hận thù & luyến tiếc

& hai miếng sắn khô

Mười bốn gương mặt hướng lên trời, nơi mây mù cất giọng xám ngắt, hát vang một giai điệu quen thuộc: *Ô ông trời ông trời / tại sao tại sao con sinh ra / tại sao hỡi trời?*

& một miếng sắn khô

Mười bốn tên cướp đói, chờ đợi, mắt đầy bụi đỏ.

Áphilatinh, thứ năm trong số mười bốn đứa con tiêu điều

Tôi là một quả trứng vỡ trên con đường hè nóng bỏng.
Là con chim rơi, sẽ bỏ mạng bên hàng rào đổ nát.
Sói rừng gườm tôi, rình rập hướng này, hướng nọ,
tính cách ăn tôi.

Không sách giáo khoa không cơm áo
chỉ một bát đầy những nỗi buồn,
một bầu trời sáng rỗng,
cùng hàng trăm mặt trời cùng nhau bốc cháy.

Họ đã giết chết màn đêm.

Có ai đang chôn người nhà ở cuối ngõ.

Này?

Người có phải mẹ tôi không? Tại sao tôi sinh ra?

Bộ xương cháy sém

nhô ra từ thịt tôi bắt đầu rít lên những câu hỏi có lửa.

Mặt trời đã lặn

mà sao trời vẫn sáng loà? Đêm đã đi đâu?

Tại sao con mắt phải của tôi bỗng dưng quay sai hướng?

Người con nhỏ nhất cất tiếng

Tôi đi tìm một gương mặt mà tôi không biết. Đâu đây có một bàn tay, một ánh mắt, một nụ cười, một mùi hương. Một an ổn. Một mát lành. Gương mặt cứ đến rồi đi, thấp thoáng như màn lụa bay ngược sáng ban trưa. Gần đây, trời nóng khô cả ngày, lúc nào cũng tưởng như ban trưa. Có tiếng chuông reo trong rừng thông, chuông reo chiêu hồn những vắng mặt & ảo ảnh. Tôi đi tìm một gương mặt mà tôi không biết. Có thể là một tổ tiên mấy đời. Có thể chính là người chú trong những chuyện cổ tích mà bà mẹ quá cố của tôi thường kể ngày xưa, người chú biết chế ngự thiên tai. Nhưng hôm nay, khi ông đến nhà thăm tôi, tôi nhận ra chiếc túi thần kỳ của ông giờ hoàn toàn trống rỗng, không còn dấu vết của sương gió càn khôn. Ông cứ đứng đó xanh xao trong khu vườn khát nước nhà tôi, với một vẻ bối rối vĩnh cửu trên mặt, và mùi băng phiến trong hơi thở buồn bã. Ông thở ra một luồng khói xanh, luồng khói bay tụ thành mây, rồi đám mây đổ xuống một dòng kêu than từ phía những quầng mặt trời hừng cháy:

Ta cũng bàng hoàng chẳng khác gì ngươi. Ở dưới kia, người chết cũng bơ vơ hệt người sống. Ta đi tìm một gương mặt mà ta không biết. Ngươi có phải mẹ ta không? Tại sao bờ sông ngập khét trong cây đổ, rễ sém và mùi của tóc cháy? Miệng túi càn khôn của ta héo cạn rồi. Ngươi muốn chạm vào nó không?

Tôi chạm, và lập tức miệng túi, cùng toàn bộ thân thể ông biến mất vào làn nắng chói loà. Một vệt bụi nóng đọng lại ngón tay tôi trong chốc lát, rồi tan vào trận cuồng phong vẫn hàng ngày thổi qua làng. Như hàng ngàn lưỡi dao câm, cơn bụi quất da tôi, làn gió cứa sâu vào làn da một bàng hoàng bất tận.

Deeper Still

Erin Latimer

Row asks what it is, and she turns to look. A gum leaf cracked jagged and burnt bronze by the sun. He puts his hand on the ground and, from stem to tip, it curves longer than the span of his pinky and thumb.

She tells him it used to flood here, when he was little. He's little now, she thinks. Boy's eight-years-old and doesn't know the living world. Leaves and grass less familiar to him than blood and bones. He knows water as mud and the sky as smoke, and the moon as a mirror for fire.

The last flood broke the waste reserves on their property seven years ago. When the water dried up, another flood was in its place: every indestructible scrap of their life laid bare, a wasteland of waste. As if she and Lou hadn't felt guilty just looking at Row, they'd had to be haunted by all the terrifyingly human-made things, that seemed terrifyingly inhuman now. Every hormone needle, spent vitamin packet, used nappy, and crusted plastic tub. All of it so stubbornly insistent on existing, as if it were worth more than her own son's heart.

And she'd thought: why did it have to get to this? She and Lou should have felt haunted all along, for it was all there all along, like the balloon from that children's film they found at the bottom of the deepest part of the ocean, when oceans had been deep and water covered most of the world.

The red ground is full of holes. It has been for so long she doesn't need to tell Row anymore to watch where he's going. He knows all the markers and leads the way across the pockmarked earth, the gum leaf stem between his finger and thumb, waving like a little flag.

She wonders where that leaf came from. Turn in a circle and you see bare horizon everywhere around, shifting with colour where the sun melts into the candle wax skin of the earth.

When she looks away from the setting sun to find her son, he is gone.

Empty red ground full of holes. Her stomach falls.

It's only a moment before she sees him, but it takes twice as long for her breath to come back. She has to remind herself that he is no longer small enough for the ground to swallow him up in one bite.

Row lies stomach down, gumboots swinging in the air. She runs to catch up with him. The boy is shoulder-deep in a hole, cheek pressed to the earth's rusty jowl.

"Dropped it," he explains. "An accident."

She pulls him out by the back of his shirt and sits down cross-legged beside him, swinging the bag of canisters from her back into her lap. She gives one to Row and watches him use two hands to twist the hybrid metal and plastic parts into place, the canister's body double the width of his arm. He pulls the cord free, wrapping the end around his palm like she showed him, before he drops the canister into the hole.

It whistles and thumps, spinning as it plummets in search of a small ocean.

Row clings to the lifeline. A layer of dust clings to his boots.

Lately it's difficult for her to look at those boots without thinking about how they'll be here long after he has outgrown them and grown up and died. The world must be full of stubborn little rubber boots that wouldn't wash away and decay. She imagines herself gathering them all up and burning them… but even fire makes a choice about what precious things it takes and what useless things it leaves behind.

Lou's watch ticks on her wrist.

Row begins to wind the cord. When the canister returns, he dumps it between his out-turned knees and untwists the bottom to release the filter tray.

In the grille lies the leaf, in two imperfect pieces.

Row lifts the pieces out one by one as if they are just-born creatures, though he's never seen anything be born. He lays one half in his open palm and the other in hers.

She remembers him just born.

If she and Lou had only known.

She reaches over and nudges the canister, reminding him to drink. Row flips the top and pulls up the spout, sipping quickly, cradling the just-born dying thing.

She often pictures Row's heart as if it lives outside his chest, thrumming with fragile warmth. A just-born dying thing.

Row holds the canister out for her.

The ocean inside only fills it halfway.

Wind rushes between them. Her fingers curl protectively around the leaf, but to her surprise Row lifts his hand and lets the wind carry his half away. It dances and disappears. He grins, gap between his teeth big and wide.

"Now it can go where it's meant," he says.

The holes they've drilled in the land whistle in a language she will never understand.

She dug her claws in like everyone else taught her, but she's learned too late that the earth doesn't unscar.

Lou's watch ticks.

We were never meant to be here forever, she thinks.

She opens her hand.

So Close to Home

Andrew Hook

They repurposed the filling stations. Trucks arrived from the North, their refrigerated steel containers insulated with compounded-melt low-density polyethylene plastic ideal for transporting frozen water. Each vehicle contained the equivalent of 1,040 to 1,250 litres. The journey length caused the contents to melt by the time destinations were reached. Not all of them got through. When they did, despite the underground storage tanks having been scrubbed and rescrubbed in readiness, the water always retained a petroleum base-note. Those trace chemicals were clearly harmful to health. It would have been good to have an alternative.

There was no alternative.

In the Southern Hemisphere there were rumours that moisture was being extracted through other means. No government sought to deny or verify. No refugees made it to our shores. There were no refugees. Water was the refugee now.

At first they were afraid the polar ice caps would melt.

And then they were afraid that they wouldn't.

Finch held two 5-litre plastic containers, one in each hand. His son—Joel, seven-years-old, a tousled scrub of black hair—clutched an old 2-litre plastic Coke bottle to his chest. The red label had faded to white. Finch knew plastic deteriorated over time, that those bottles would start leaching chemicals into the water and that they shouldn't be reused. This knowledge was redundant now.

He ran a tongue over cracked lips. His dehydrated body wasn't producing enough saliva. There were those he knew who had developed plaque, tooth decay and gum disease. They had mouth sores, yeast infections. If he were to run his fingers through Joel's hair they would stick like sick in carpet. Just a few more steps and they would be under the filling station canopy and out of the sun. Behind them, the line stretched backwards; a motley shadow.

It was mid-morning. When Finch had awoken at five, he opened the back door, knelt on the withered vegetation, and ran his tongue over the grass in the hope of morning dew. Failing that, he roused Joel and they left the house. Their nearest filling station was under a mile away.

Joel never complained. Finch realised that, at his age, he had accepted the tragedy and was yet to apportion blame. Finch had mitigated the death of the boy's mother as much as he could. The boy was barely parsing grief. The battle for survival trumped the poetics of relationships.

Diesel was reserved for the trucks, the army and the police. There was barely traffic noise. In another life Finch would have welcomed the quiet. His head had always been busy: his wife, the newborn, the low rumble of the washing machine, tumble dryer, or fan extractor in their tiny-terraced home. The television always screening whether there was somebody watching or not. The neighbour's music, their lawnmowers, their parties.

Only the arguments remained—often rising to a pitch in a mutational falsetto. Crazy, nonsensical fights that dried out the throat and ended as abruptly as they began. Yet at 5am there was nothing but footsteps on the tarmac, the surface softly peeling with a wet slap against the sole as the day grew older and hotter.

Before the rationing Finch had made a mean fried rice. Quartered button mushrooms in sunflower oil, a little fish sauce, a little soy. Two tins of canned sardines in tomato sauce. Into the wok with a few taps of a wooden spoon to disconnect those edible bones. Another dash of soy sauce, then cooked jasmine rice and spring onions while he cracked an egg in another pan, the yellow sat in white like a glacial sun. More soy sauce, some hot chilli sauce, and then on the plate, half-mooned by sliced cucumber with the egg on top. Now anything salty was a burden, potentially harmful. Nevermind that Finch sometimes opened his cabinets and eyed the fish sauce, his mouth so parched he might down it in one. The treachery of liquid, the mockery of the sea. Even the chilli sauce had become an enemy.

They moved forwards in the queue. No one spoke. It was inadvisable to do so. Armed guards stood by each pump. Finch glanced at those around him. A ragtail mix of ages, colours and creeds. Several like himself were accompanied by children. None were babies. Finch was close enough now to see the white containers of those at the front of the queue darkening to grey as nozzles at the pumps filled them. There was no charge for this—yet. Finch knew it couldn't be long before there would be. Already there was a certain *discernment* between different echelons of society. The promise for everyone to be treated equally could only be kept while it was sustainable. Thereafter, society would jostle into familiar positions.

Finch remembered the initial news reports. The scientist who warned of the crisis and the prime minister who nodded. The nod which evolved into a condescending smile that undermined the science, to add that, even though water had always comprised 70% of the Earth, only one percent was *ever* fresh and usable. As if water were constantly scarce, as though the world had always been in crisis. Finch noticed the scientist expel a sigh. His warning mitigated. The announcement then followed by the weather.

Finch turned his thoughts to Africa, Australia: those perpetual television images of cracked earth and flies on lips. He had tried to imagine this here. He had spoken to his wife:

"This is madness, surely?"

"Maybe." Her eyes were wide, unaccentuated by make-up. "But there's always madness. Some generations are protected from it, others aren't."

"I worry about the boy."

She raised her eyes to the ceiling, as if it were transparent and Joel's sleeping form visible—curled foetus-like, his tiny hands clutching his stuffie as though it might transport him beyond his dinosaur duvet and into some exciting new realm.

"I worry about him too."

*

Joel left the house while his father slept. The night was hot, a real burner. He wore a once-white vest top and faded blue shorts. Finch had become lax with him of late, reasoning that it was too restrictive to keep the boy inside all the time, that even apocalypse kids had to explore.

Joel's ninth birthday had passed without mention. He spent an afternoon poking a stick into the dry riverbed. Some kid told him there were frogs down there, hibernating in case the rains should return. But Joel consulted the brittle pages of his encyclopaedia and knew that wasn't true. It was the desert frogs of Australia that might emerge from underground—once every twenty years—after sensing the thrum of water. During dry spells, those frogs hibernated a metre or more below the surface, surviving in a cocoon that held water in the layers of their skin. So it wasn't amphibians that Joel was seeking, only methods to replace boredom.

Towards the end of the afternoon, he'd tagged along with a group of older kids. There were no politics here, no leaders. Each was exhausted in their own way. Starving in others. Camaraderie held them. They told stories of moisture, of mirage. Tales of vampires, bloodsuckers. Some remembered days playing with garden hoses, spraying water, soaking clothes with abandon. Now, said one of the older boys, with a conspiratorial wink, even the women were drying up.

Joel didn't understand the ins and the outs, the hand-me-down jokes, but when he suggested the plan, they listened. The trucks made pre-determined journeys, not dissimilar to the passage of water down a mountainside in the golden days. From the source they spread, fanned along tributaries, turned where the land grooved. In Joel's city they arrived in the early hours, twin orbs lighting darkness. In amongst the metalwork at the rear of the garage Joel found the tyre iron he had hidden three days ago. Gripping it in his right hand he left to join the others.

The water had gotten rust-coloured of late, a certain metallic taste, discernibly thicker texture. Rumours abounded that it was doctored on location. Joel heard a group of men with careless mouths discuss what happened in the before-times. One laughed, a disconcertingly sad almost-growl, when he phrased that, like beer, it had been *watered-down*. The others were sober at this. The concept lost on Joel.

Finch hushed that greater quantity and quality went to the rich. People were becoming more talkative in the lines. Dissonance was bubbling. The country was on the brink.

Joel only wanted what they deserved. Fair shares for everyone. The innocence of a child. Under the old aqueduct—irony unknown—they spread out. The motorway connected the city there, in which was once an accident blackspot. Now that the only vehicles were government, they were determined to create one again.

The boys were eighteen in number. Guthrie

took Joel's plan, expanded it. The curve of the sliproad exiting the motorway meant the truck would already be slowing down. Guthrie had a battered kid's bike that he placed on the highway. Joel lay on the tarmac, snug, one arm extended, his face turned in the opposite direction. There was no fear, no protection. But there was no shame in looking away if the truck didn't stop.

A mile off Finch turned in his sleep. His arm reaching out in a similar fashion, muscle memory to touch a wife who no longer existed.

The boys waited in darkness. Nine on one side, eight on the other. Illumination kept to a minimum by the display of a digital watch shielded in a cupped hand.

When it came, the truck's brakes tore the air as if ripping reality's fabric, echoing under the brick of the aqueduct. Joel was bathed in light, his shadow extending supernaturally along the tarmac, as if he were a monster forming from rising tar.

Then there was silence until the cab door opened. Joel sensed the closeness of footsteps, tentative, impatient. At a whistle he swung his arm backwards, connected the tyre iron with an ankle, snapped it.

What was intended to be a group effort became a free for all. The kids swarmed the truck, the predominant sound the buckling of empty plastic vessels as they collided in haste. The driver had a mate the boys quickly despatched. Joel didn't see what became of him. Frustration rose as the boys pressed and depressed buttons. Eventually they congregated at the rear of the truck, took turns at battering, then levering the lock.

When the doors opened, they were deluged. A tsunami disgorged. Joel's clothes stuck in an approximation of sweat. The smell was visceral, animal. The plastic bottles were filled black in the no-light by the boys who could care, while others stood mouths open in anticipation, some throwing themselves to the ground in the ever-increasing pool that appeared rust-coloured via the clamouring of the early morning light.

It was then that Joel realised the men were wrong. It wasn't that water was being tampered with at the pumps. It was a less potable liquid that was being transported then diluted. In the dark it didn't matter. The boys were face to ground and they lapped it up.

And in that moment their thirst was quenched and they sang.

Apabila Air Berhenti

Audrey Chin

(Malay translation of 'When the Water Stops'—with illustrations)

Apabila iklim berubah, ia melemparkan kebakaran belukar kepada mereka dan rebut debu yang melanda keluarga-keluarga. Pondok-pondok di hancurkan ke tanah. Setelah itu, terjadi kemarau. Semua lembu dan biri-biri dikeringkan hanya kulitnya, kemudian tinggalkan rangka.

Pada mulanya, penduduk kampung bergilir-gilir berdarah, berkongsi mimpi dan ketakutan, memahami mereka adalah manusia yang sama. Tetapai isipadu darah lelaki dewasa biasa adalah lima liter sahaja — kehilangan 40% daripada jumlah itu membawa maut. Ambang 39% hanya mempunyai 92% air di dalamnya. Selebihnya dihanyutkan oleh glukosa dan hormone, protein, lemak, vitamin, garam mineral dan karbon dioksida. Apa faedah nya? Karbon dioksida boleh menyebabkan pening, keletihan, kerengsaan, sawan atau koma. Jadi, dengan segala pertimbangan, berapa banyak air akan dituai daripada darah untuk dikongsi bersama saudara saudari di kampung?

Mereka renung-renung persoalan ini dalam hati mereka, dan pada masa yang sama sukarelawan yang telah menderma darah untuk jiran mereka, menghisap daun, getah kaktus, buah ara dan semut api selepas empat hingga lapan minggu. Namun pada akhir masa pemulihan itu, mereka masih belum cukup kuat berdarah kali

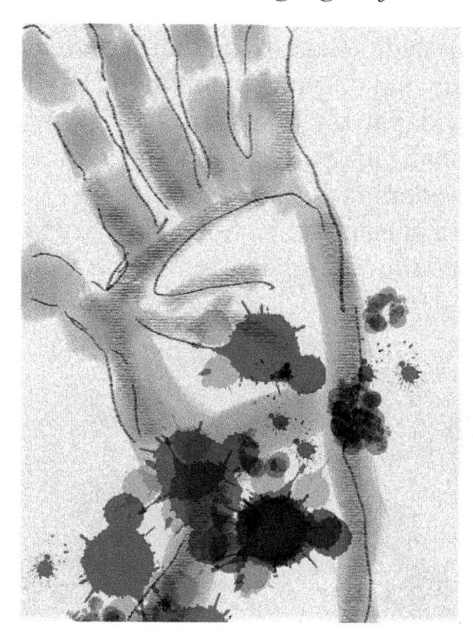

kedua apabila tibagiliran mereka. Apa yang telah dikurangkan tidak dapat diganti.

Caption:
But even the drawing of sticks stopped eventually / Tetapi walaupun membuang undi-undi kayu akhirnya pun berhenti

Jadi, apabila mereka asalnya sukarela, kini mereka membuang undi-undi kayu. Dengan cara ini, hasilnya bergantung pada tuah biasa, atau nasib terlepas. Ranting kayu adalah ranting kayu. Ranting pendek adalah pendek. Jika anda mendapatnya, nasib anda telah ditakdirkan. Satu-satunya, keselesaan anda ialah kematian ini bukanlah kematian kesepian, ia adalah pengorbanan memenuhi keperluan masyarakat.

Tetapi walaupun membuang undi-undi kayu akhirnya pun berhenti. Ini ia-lah pengorbanan yang terlalu besar. Jadi sekarang adalah masalah. Kini, mereka yang kaya, atau mempunyai kayu yang lebih besar, dapat memutuskan siapa yang akan dibunuh; dapat menentukan abu siapa yang akan terapung ke-udara.

Ia itu abu secara kiasan sahaja. Sebenarnya, apa yang berlaku, berlaku di dalam tong-tong dan baldi besar.

Caption:
Right there in the heat shimmer, awash with memories / Berendam di balut dalam kilauan panas penuh dengan kenangan

Perempuan di dalam tong

Dia berendam
di dalam mangkuk gergasi
di balut dalam kilauan panas
penuh dengan kenangan
mengantuk dan bermimpi
segala-gala
perlahan-lahan

bila berfikir
kembali masa ini
apa yang dia akan ingat?

asap berpusar
seperti awan kebajikan
membisikan di dalam sa-hutan kabus:
di manakah dia sekarang?

jiwa ia-lah
sa-bintang
paling terang di langit

sekarang dia berdarah
esok hanyalah hasrat

Perdana Menteri Negara

Sepuluh tahun yang lalu, Tuan Menteri itu telah keluar dari tempat perlindungannya. Tuan berazam menduduki di tangga muzium yang didedikasikan untuk Paus. Pada hari itu, beberapa pemimpin hak asasi manusia, hakim mahkamah dan ibu bapa warga muda telah memerhati terpegun ketika mereka melihat Tuan menolak keluar bibirnya dan mengangkat kitab Bible agama selama satu minit penuh sebagai kamera tersentak. Dan semasa Tuan mengumumkan program baru untuk menuai air, adalah polis antirusuhan memakai topeng gas dan membawa belantan serta senjata dengan peluru getah sudah menyerangkan aktivis membawa slogan cinta dan keamanan.

Caption: What was a drop of blood? / Apakah setitik dara, Tuan bertanya?

Apakah setitik darah, Tuan bertanya? Pastinya ekonomi mengatasi segala-galanya. Mengapa perlu ada pergolakan awam apabila stok meningkat? Adakah mereka melihat kenaikan 267 mata Dow hari ini? Dan kemajuan Komposit Nasdaq? Pasti mereka paham teori evolusi tentang pemilihan gen yang berkemungkinan meninggalkan salinan terbanyak?

Bertahun-tahun selepas itu, dalam alam semesta yang benar benar berubah sepenuhnya, setiap ketua biskop yang telah marah atas penyalahgunaan kemudahan ibadat sepuluh tahun yang lalu, akan mengingati pelanggaran prinsip sifat manusia itu dan mengeluarkan empat perkataan yang tercungap semasa mereka duduk di dalam tong: Saya. Tidak. Boleh. Bernafas.

Sedih nasib ketua-ketua itu, Tuan Menteri mengaku sendiri. Tetapi protes sentiasa hodoh, fikir Tuan. Apatah lagi, pilihan raya akan tiba.

Puan kaya di kota

'Apabila air berhenti, darah mesti mengalir,' katakan Puan kaya dengan gelang berlian pelangi mengelilingi tangannya. Kerongsang bernilai satu billion dollar nya — satu set dengan loket aurora — adalah hadiah daripada sepupu kepada sepupu, seorang yang namanya Puan cuba diingat tetapi tidak boleh. Usaha itu terlalu sukar.

Puan ini berjaya daripada bencana orang lain. Kehidupanya berkembang kerana menyusu dari orang yang tidak penting, sama seperti pengemis di bilik bawah tanahnya. Dari kampung, naratif mereka adalah sesuatu yang Puan tidak percaya; sa-jenis cerita yang dicerminkan oleh ahli sejarah seni dalam foto lama. Kisah-kisah yang Puan boleh terima adalah yang menimbulkan Hitler, Mussolini dan Idi Amin Dada. Bukan salah Puan jika pengemis itu tidak berada dalam gambaran yang hampir sempurna. Mereka seperti kenangan memalukan yang berubah setiap kali Puan melihat, kenangan yang kesilapan, yang tidak pernah kelihatan nyata. Puan boleh dapat banyak buku mengenai perkara sebegini; tetapi masih sukar.

'Matikan rintihan mereka!' Puan jerit pada hambanya. Bunyi erangan mereka bukan hitam mahupun putih. Ia tidak mematuhi peraturan komposisi. Jika tangisan mereka adalah persoalan, itu adalah persoalan dalam bahasa Babylon yang Puan tidak memahami. Vokal, suku kata, sintaksis, perumpamaan atau konteks . . . Mustahil untuk Puan cuba! Ia terlalu sukar!

Apa yang tidak sukar untuk dipahami ia-lah produk vintaj dengan aroma yang luar biasa. Lebih baik lagi, darah dari kampung tulen tidak tercemar oleh pencemaran bandar dan datang pada harga yang berpatutan. Darah kampung menggabungkan keasidan yang betul dengan bau asap dan lada yang harum, semua terpancar daripada cecair ungu yang terkandung dalam bekas loyang.

'Ia sukar tetapi tidak ada acara lain. Darah vintaj mesti mengalir untuk kemandirian kita,' katakan Puan sambil memeluk anak kucing dengan penuh kasih sayang.

Masalah seorang suami di kampung

Apabila dia menyadari apa masalahnya, dia mendapat pencerahan. Ini masalah yang dicipta oleh pemandangan empat belas kanak-kanak lapar dan tiga keropok ubi kering. Adegan inilah yang membuatkan dia bertanya soalan, 'Bini atau anak?'

Dia bukan jenis orang yang suka mencari kesalahan atau menyimpan dendam. Tetapi, mungkin dia dipengaruhi oleh kebencian dan penyesalan setiap hari yang mengunjung kehidupan rumah tangga orang miskin. Mungkin sebab perasaan-perasaan ini telah menyelinap masuk fikirannya seperti kerdil dan berkembang menjadi perosak: mencuri, menyerang dan semua itu. Mungkin inilah sebabnya, dia sampai kesimpulan bininya ialah orang yang menjadikan kanak-kanak wujud dan memulakan meraka hidup kitaran yang menyakitkan mereka. Atau mungkin, ketakutan yang menentukan pilihannya . . .

Apabila pencerahan bininya tiba, tidak ada keraguan tentang soalan yang diajukan. Ia adalah, 'Suami atau anak?'

Si suami yang lebih tegas. Maaf, katanya, tetapi apa yang berlaku dalam tong dan baldi besar berlaku dengan cepat. Maka, dia bertindak.

Selepas itu, dia merindui seorang untuk ditegur. Tetapi kini ada cukup wang memberi makan kepada kanak-kanak lapar: Si bongsu hanya dua tahun; Afia, anak yang lahir pada hari Jumaat; Abinbola, dilahirkan orang kaya tetapi sentiasa miskin; Amara, yang dulu anggun tetapi sekarang perut buncit dan botak dengan kwashiokor; Chi, Ke, Re, Po, empat kembar mempunyai rambut nilon dan mata penuh dengan pasir . . . Ya masih ada empat belas pilihan. Ya, yang si dia yang lebih tegas, yang bertindak!

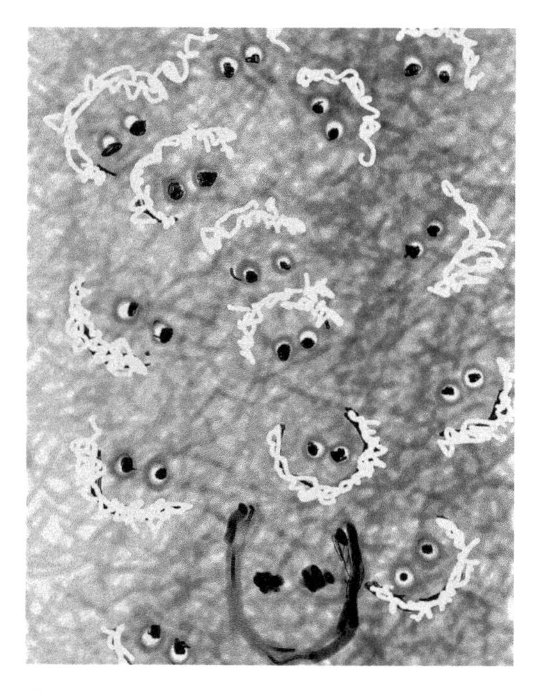

Caption: Fourteen options still /
Masih ada empat belas pilihan

Afia, kelima daripada 14 belas kanak-kanak tanpa ibu

saya
adalah telur pecah di jalan yang menggelegak
saya
seekor burung akan mati di pagar kawat berduri
sini
serigala berlari kesana kemari
menimbang bagaimana memakan
saya.

rasa rinduku kembali
tiada sekolah
tiada nasi
tiada kuah
hanya langit kosong bersiul
ketika kami menguburkan orang orang mati.
saya
adalah kad bertanda titik merah
menunggu anak panah menembut

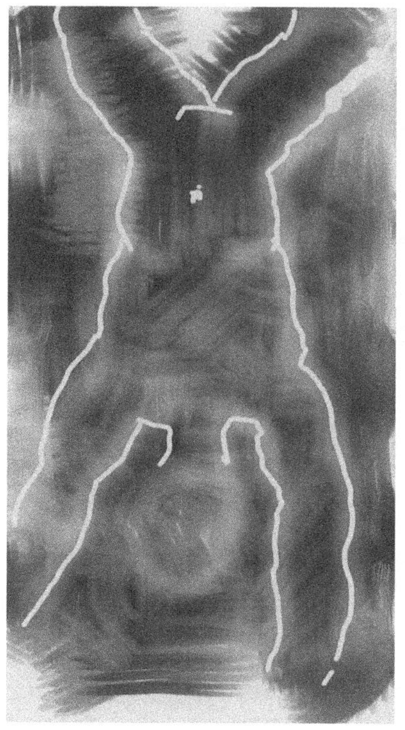

Caption: An empty sky whistling / Hanya langit kosong bersiul

saya
adalah mata
air pancut ker-
ing
sini
adalah anak
yatim ibu saya
adakah awak
ibu
saya?
sana
adalah
seekor ular be-
ludak
rangka ter-
perangkap da-
lam desisannya
sana
adalah bulu
kelabu berpusat
tetapi
di mana ba-
dan burung nya?

Caption: A skeleton trapped in a black mamba's hissing / Seekor ular beludak rangka terperangkap dalam desisannya

Kataan anak bongsu

Saya sedang mencari sesuatu yang saya belum alami — tangan menyentuh tanganku, mata merenungku, seorang tersenyum kepada saya, haruman seorang yang disayangi. Ia adalah keselesaan dan kehangatan.

ada
wajah yang muncul dan pudar
cinta yang retak
rumit dan berbahaya
kabur dan runtu

Saya sedang mengingat sesuatu yang saya ingin melupa - pakcik dengan karung-karung kosong, bau gegat dalam nafasnya, matanya benteng terhadap harapan.

Saat-saat ini kembali berulang kali, setiap ingatan penuh dengan harapan dunia akan ingat berbeza.

Stories from the Sandpaper Tongue

Oz Hardwick

i. Life on Mars

Wells parched with minus signs grate on every plaza, their sums irrefutable as a child waving two fingers in your face. It's a kind of victory without a parade; a kind of peace without forgiveness; a kind of caress without kindness. It's the question and answer of an echo down a long stone shaft, a dropped coin without a splash. Taps shudder a morse code of empty retching and dog breath from the desert that was yesterday a garden. See how they grow. See how they go. See? How late it is to be rattling buckets and laying out the best china in hope of just the right kind of rain. How late it is to be laying down the law about washing away responsibilities and the red dust that gets everywhere. Plus or minus, take it or leave it: a well without water's just an exit wound, and all the tissues in the world won't staunch its juddering flow.

ii. The Hunters

Water runs but can't hide, its skin glistening on the dry ground. We send out hunters with binoculars and bows, draped in camouflage that only makes them a different kind of obvious. Some don't come back, and most of those who do are changed beyond recognition: they are younger, with tighter flesh and different tastes in clothing and preferences for more or less spicy food. Most return with round eyes that dart like birds, while others have developed forked tongues. Scales, fur, feathers, are all common mutations. In truth, water never wanted to hide—never even noticed our pursuit—and when we see it, head back and laughing, coursing across a strangled plain, it bears no mind to our jeeps and horses, our boasts and traps, our all-consuming need; but we follow just the same, be it forty days or a thousand and one nights, just to bring back stories our tongues are too parched to tell.

iii. Subterranean

Bolt holes burn with a taste like blood, with a taste like excuses, with a taste like a tin cup scraped on rock in lines that wave like water. Water is the word that even ghosts won't utter, as they stutter in the darkness, pretending it's light. The lackey and the leader bleed into each other, dry as, dry as—dust? Four skeletal horses bolt, riderless, through the world's empty gut, stiff as old paint, and a blind child who trusts in everything reminds us we are ghosts.

Maji Yanapotuama

Aldegunda Matoyo

(Swahili translation of 'When the Water Stops')

Katika mabadiliko ya tabia nchi, kulitokea joto kali sana na kusababisha cheche za moto zilizounguza vichaka, na baadhi ya nyumba zilizoezekwa kwa nyasi zilishika moto na kuteketeza vibanda hadi chini na kubakia majivu, dhoruba za vumbi ambazo zilisambaratisha familia kuweza kukaa, ukame—ng'ombe, mbuzi na kondoo wote walitoweka, kufa na kuoza na wengine kukondeana na kubakia mfupa na ngozi na baadhi kubakia mifupa tu. Mwanzoni, wanakijiji hawakutilia maanani na walipuuza hali hiyo ila walianza kutaharuki hali ilipozidi kuwa mbaya kwa kuona watu na mifugo wanakufa sana ndipo wakaanza kuhofu, wakielewa sasa hiyo hali sio ya kawaida na itawakumba wote, hivyo itawabidi waungane wawe wamoja kuweza kukabiliana na hali hiyo.

Kwa kawaida binadamu mtu mzima ana ujazo wa damu wa lita tano—upungufu wa asilimia arobaini ni hatari sana na huweza kusababisha kifo. Kizingiti cha asilimia thelathini na tisa kina maji ya asilimia tisini na mbili tu ndani yake; vingine huoshwa katika glukosi, homoni, protini, mafuta, vitamini, madini chumvi na kaboni dioksidi—je, faida yake ni nini? Kaboni dioksidi mwilini inaweza kusababisha kizunguzungu, uchovu, kuweweseka, kizunguzungu, degedege au kukosa fahamu. Kwa hiyo, kutokana na athari hiyo, ni kiasi gani cha maji kingesalia kuweza kukidhi mahitaji ya kijiji kizima?

Wanakijiji walijiuliza sana swali hilo akilini mwao na wasipate majibu, huku baadhi yao wakijitolea kwa ajili ya ukoo wao, na kuanza kunyonya majani ya mkaratusi na utomvu, tini na mchwa wa jangwani kwa muda wa wiki nne hadi nane hivi. Lakini bado hawakuwa na nguvu za kutosha za kuweza kutoa damu zaidi awali yao ilipofika tena. Hasara hii haikuweza kuvumilika na kujazwa tena.

Pale ambapo wale waliokuwa wamejitolea, sasa wakaanza kuokota vijiti ili kufanya mchezo wa bahati nasibu kuona kama ni vya bahati ya pata potea. Vijiti vikawa vijiti, vifupi vikazidi kuwa vifupi. Utakapo okota kijiti, hapo ndipo hatma yako itakapoamuliwa, faraja yako pekee inakuwa kwamba kifo hicho hakitakuwa cha kwako pekee bali cha ushirika ambao mlijitolea kukidhi mahitaji ya jamii nzima.

Mchezo huo wa vijiti hatimae ulifikia tamati na ikaamuliwa kuanza kutoa watu kafara. Hii ilikuwa ni dhabihu kubwa mno. Kwa hiyo sasa lilikuwa jambo la maamuzi kwa wale wenye pesa, mali au wenye mamlaka makubwa zaidi, kuamua nani wa kumuua na kumtoa kafara.

Na hiyo ingeamuliwa majivu ya mtu yupi yatakaoyorushwa angani, na kusema kuwa hiyo ni njia ya mojawapo ya mfano. Kilichotokea kweli sasa kilifanyika kwenye njia ya mavazi.

Mwanamke ndani ya vazi

Atakachofanya wiki hii ni kukaa kwenye bakuli, pale pale kwenye mng'aro wa joto la kumetameta huku akiwa anaelea kwenye wimbi la mawazo. Akiwa amejaa kumbukumbu huku anasinzia, anapanga na kupangua na vyote hivyo vinamjia kwa mwendo wa taratibu. Akitafakari cha kuangalia kwa wakati huo aliopo, atakumbuka nini hata kwa baadae? Akawa anatazama tu moshi unavyoelea juu na kuzunguka kama vile unakumbatiana kwenye kumbatio la mwenye fadhili, likiunda mawingu makubwa makubwa yakibubujikwa na maneno kama: *Uko wapi sasa?* Nafsi yake ni chombo kinachong'aa zaidi mawinguni. Leo anavuja damu huku kesho akiitamani.

Kiongozi wa Taifa

Miaka kumi iliyopita, alijitokeza kiongozi mwenye nguvu kutoka kwenye makazi yake, akiwa amedhamiria kuteka na kutawala katika hekalu lililofunguliwa kama jumba la makumbusho ya Papa. Aliwapiga butwaa viongozi wa haki za binadamu, mahakama kuu na akina mama wengi pale aliponyanyua mdomo wake na kuinua juu Biblia kwa dakika moja huku wapiga picha wakikazana na kamera zao kunasa kilichokuwa kinajiri. Askari polisi wa kutuliza ghasia wakiwa na fimbo, virungu, risasi za mpira na vinyago vya gesi waliwafata waandamanaji wa amani waliokuwa wakitangaza kauli mbiu inayohusu sanaa ya kuthamini na upendo.

Kulikuwa na maana gani kumwaga damu wakati uchumi wenyewe ulizidi machafuko ya raia na hisa zilipanda juu? Je, uliona Dow, ina faida ya pointi 267? Na maendeleo kwenye mchanganyiko wa Nasdaq? Nadharia ya mageuzi yote haya ilikuwa ni sababu ya uteuzi wa asili wa muundo ambao ungeacha nakala zake nyingi.

Miaka ya mwanga ilikuwepo na kila askofu mkuu kwenye ulimwengu mbadala, alipandwa na hasira ya matumizi mabaya ya mwenendo wa kuabudu ibada, na kuzingatia ukiukwaji wa kihistoria kuhusu kanuni za ubinadamu na kutamka maneno matatu yenye kugawanyika: Mimi. Siwezi. Kupumua.

Maandamano huwa na taswira mbaya, aliwaza kiongozi huyo. Na uchaguzi mpya ulikuwa mbioni unakuja.

Mwanamke tajiri kwenye jiji kuu

Maji yanapoacha kutiririka, damu lazima iendelee kuzunguka, anajisemea mwanamke mwenye bangili ya almasi yenye umbo la upinde wa mvua iliyozunguka mkono wake. Broshi hii yenye thamani ya mabilioni ya dola, ilikuwa ni kati ya seti na yenye mvuto mzuri kama kishaufu iliyokuwa ni zawadi kutoka kwa binamu wa binamu wa mjomba wake mkubwa ambae hakuweza kukumbuka jina lake kwa kuwa lilikuwa ni gumu mno kulitamka.

Ananawiri kutokana na majanga ya watu wengine. Anastawi kutoka kwa wasio na umuhimu kwake. Kama watu waliokuwepo kwenye pishi lake, ombaomba waliotokea kijijini. Hiyo kwao ni simulizi ambalo hakutaka kukubaliana nalo, na ni zile hadithi za kale ambazo zipo kwenye picha za zamani za wanahistoria wa sanaa. Muonekano wa vazi lake ni kama lile la kisiasa ambalo liliwapaisha watu kama kina Hitler, Mussolini na Idi Amin Dada. Na hakujali endapo hao watu hawakufaa kuwa kwenye kundi hilo la watu maarufu. Hao watu kwenye pishi walikuwa ni makosa mabaya sana ambayo yanaelea katika sura tofauti tofauti kila mara akiiangalia ambayo kamwe sio hali halisi. Pia kuna vitabu vingi mno vinavyohusu ubinadamu, lakini hali ni ngumu!

Hebu zimeni hizo kelele za hao wanaonung'unika! Aling'aka na kuwafokea wafanyakazi wake huku akisonya. Mnung'uniko wao hata haueleweki kama ni wa maonevu au uchovu na ni ambao hautii sheria za utungaji. Ikiwa kilio chao ni swali, basi itakuwa ni kilio katika lugha ya Babeli ambayo haelewi wanachosema, hata vokali zake hazijui, silabi, matamshi hata mafumbo, na haiwezekani kujaribu kwa sababu ni ngumu sana!

Kilicho rahisi kuelewa ni kwamba mavuno ya hao kwenye pishi huja na harufu nzuri puani. Hao watu waliokuja kutoka kijijini walikuja kwa bei nzuri na damu yao ni safi, haijachakachuliwa na kuchafuliwa na hewa ya jiji kuu. Damu ya kijijini inachanganyikana na asidi sahihi na harufu nzuri ya moshi. Nyama ya nguruwe na pilipili, urujuani ni ambavyo vimeviringishwa ndani ya shaba.

Na damu safi na salama lazima iendelee kuzunguka ndani ya uhai wa vizazi vyake vyote. Anambembeleza kwa upendo kitoto cha mbwa cha aina ya labradoodle karibu na kwenye titi lake.

Mume wa kijiji mwenye shinikizo

Mapinduzi yalikuja pale alipodokezwa na kushauriwa akubaliane nayo.

Ilikuwa ni sababu iliyoundwa kutafakari, midomo kumi na nne yenye njaa, kuilisha kwa kuwagawia biskuti tatu zilizotengenezwa kwa mihogo mikavu ambayo ilibidi ipitishe kwa wote waile na kushiba. Hiyo ikawa sababu iliyomfanya ajiulize swali: Je, mke au watoto? Huyo mke aliwaleta duniani na kufanya uwepo wao hapa. Hao watoto walianzisha mzunguko wa maisha ambao ulikuwa ni wa mateso.

Labda, hii ndo sababu iliyomsababishia huyo mume awe ni mtu katili, anatoa kila siku sauti za chuki, majuto... Hizo chuki na majuto zilinyata kama nyani mbilikimo wasionekane na waligeuka kuwa kama wadudu: waliiba, walipora, walivamia, walikaba na uhalifu wa kila aina. Huyo mume hakuwa mtu wa kuweka kinyongo pamoja na kwamba ndoa yake ilikuwa yenye huzuni, kwa maana hiyo ilikuwa ni sahihi kusema kwamba hofu ndo ilikuwa imemtanda na kumtawala na kumsababishia kufanya maamuzi yake ya kipekee. Kwani pale mabadiliko na maamuzi ya mkewe yatakapokuja, hapakuwa na swali lolote kuhusiana na ukweli ulipolalia: amchague mume au watoto?

Huyo mume alisababisha yeye mambo yote hayo yatokee, ndiyo. Pole. Wanasema kilichotokea kwenye vazi kilikuwa kama radi na ilikuwa kwa haraka sana ambayo haikutegemewa.

Sasa hivi bila mke alikosa mtu wa kumpigia kelele. Ila kulikuwa na pesa za kutosha za kuweza kulisha watoto wenye njaa kwa muda huo, na wadogo walikuwa wawili tu. Afia, mtoto aliyezaliwa Ijumaa. Abimbola, mtoto aliyezaliwa tajiri lakini maskini siku zote. Amara, alikuwa ni mrembo sana, ila kwa sasa ana upara, tumbo kubwa na kwashiakoo. Chi, Ke, Re, Po, mapacha wanne wenye nywele za nailoni na macho yaliyojaa mchanga muda wote.

Alifanya mambo yote hayo yatokee kwa sababu, baada ya mke wake... kulikuwa na maamuzi mengine kumi na nne yaliyokuwa yanamsubiri.

Afia, mtu wa tano kati ya kumi na wanne wasio na mama

Mimi ni yai lililovunjika kwenye barabara yenye makorongo. Ndege aliyefia kwenye uzio wa nyaya zilizozungushiwa nyembe kila kona. Mbweha akinizungukia huku na huko, akitafakari atakavyo nila na kunitafuna kwa uchu. Shauku yangu imerudi tena, hakuna shule, hakuna supu. Ni mawingu matupu angani yanayopiga binja na miluzi tunapozika marehemu wetu. Mimi ni kadi iliyotiwa alama—doa jekundu hutia alama popote pale. Mshale utakaopita kwa haraka na kuingia kwenye jicho la chemchemi iliyokauka. Wewe ni mama yangu? Kuna mifupa iliyotegwa na kunaswa na kuzomewa na mamba mweusi. Pia kuna manyoya ya kijivu yanayozunguka kwa njia ambayo siyo sahihi.

Mtoto mdogo kuliko wote aongea

Nipo nachakura chakura natafuta kitu nisichokijua. Kuna mkono na macho, tabasamu na harufu. Kuna faraja, kuna joto. Ila sina kumbukukumbu yoyote ya sura inayoniijia na kutoweka, haya ni mapenzi yaliyo na ufa. Hayaeleweki, sio salama. Hayaonekani vizuri, yana ukungu na yanaashiria kubomoka.

Upweke unatawala na upo kama mjomba mkubwa aliyebeba magunia matupu, na ana harufu ya mipira ya nondo kwenye pumzi lake, macho yake ni ngome dhidi ya matumaini. Unafikiria muda huu, tena na tena, na kutamani wewe na dunia nzima ungefikiria tofauti.

NEW(er) Water

Clara Chow

Turbidity. Tur-bee-dee-tee. Say it together with me, children. *Turbidity.*

The daughters and sons of the rich island-state learn the vocabulary first. Sitting at their tiny desks, in the middle of clean-room kindergartens, under the glare of energy-efficient LED lights, the little ones parrot their teachers. Wrapping their tongues around the terminology that has made their city the most powerful on Earth. Tasting the syllables of wealth and influence. They cock their innocent heads and try again, harder. The words are slippery in their mouths. They taste astringent and bitter like chlorine. Metallic like copper. Attack the nostrils like ammonia. The little kids blink away stunned tears as the teacher uncorks vials of chemicals and waves them in the air. Only an involuntary reaction. They sit with their legs hooked around the legs of chained chairs. With clenched fists on their hot laps.

Total Trihalomethanes. After me, now. *Heterotrophic Plate Count.* Very good.

Thirty years in the classroom. Increasingly, these days, Hayat has been experiencing out-of-body experiences while drilling his young charges in the state-mandated job training. Hovering over it all, his back stuck by sweat to the rough plaster of the false ceiling, he looks down at the smooth tops of his students' heads—so many slick, brown button mushrooms—and feels something like regret.

What happened to the enthusiastic shouts of *EH!* The bursting forth of *BEE!* And the simple joy of shrieking *SEA*, rocking on small rumps with so much energy? Up with the relentless LED bulbs that will last a hundred years, Hayat wriggles uncomfortably like a pinned beetle. Summoned by his nostalgia for the alphabet, an image of the sea appears in his mind. The endless waves, clear and turquoise, stretching between each human being in the nation. Lapping at his conscience.

He looks down at himself, in his Dri-fit Unilateral Newer Ecological suit, the dark maroon of its powder-coated fabric-chrome surface giving him the appearance of a bloodied warrior. Standard-issue for all NEW(er) Water Inc. employees. He crosses his arms across his naked chest, dangling from the ceiling. Is he still inside the suit, face hidden by his visor, or is he up here? How many of him are there? How much cubic millimetres of moisture is he losing, if he is indeed out of his suit and not hallucinating? How many hours, days, before he shrivels up like a starfish in an oven and dies?

Whatever. The bell rings. Hayat stands before the class, staring dumbly at his gloved hands. He turns them over and reads the stats on his wrists. There is still water. There is still time. The closed system, his body terrarium, is still functioning as normal.

"Class dismissed," he says.

The children scrape their chairs back, their DUNE suits glowing translucent pink, purple and aqua, like jellyfish. Phosphorescent offspring. The hope of President, Country and Guild. There is no time for childhood. The world's water crisis awaits. Each dawn brings with it the race to sell the state's patented waste-water recycling and desalinisation technology to the other countries clamouring at their door. Treaties to be inked, trade deals to be negotiated, equipment to be maintained. Money never sleeps. The water-recycling cycle continues.

Thirty years on the job—first as a technician, then as a sales gallery guide for foreign dignitaries with a view to buy, a senior aide in the marketing department, and then, his final posting, as a trainer—and Hayat knows the drill. The closed system that is also the State New(er) Water Guild. Nothing gets in or out. Every bit of corporate intellectual property accounted for and recirculated within iron-clad doors, digital firewalls and augmented-reality hatches. Like the DUNE suits, so water-tight that waste-matter reverts to drinking water and is fed intravenously into the wearer, who is sealed into one from birth and pried from it by the mortician.

The classroom door beeps as he leaves, logging the end of his shift.

He drifts back to his office-bunk.

To control the prices, the State Guild has to regulate supply, too. Demand, naturally, takes care of itself. Nothing lives without the guild's product. Hayat has heard of the less fortunate places that have resorted to blood-letting and vampirism. Hayat himself wrote the propaganda:

> *Imagine a world without NEW(er) Water. No, you won't be able to. Your brain would be a raisin in days. Enquire NOW about our payment plan – we can help with loan applications for economies or other stimulus packages!*

He also wrote the employee rulebook during a short stint in HR:

> *Officers of the Guild caught providing company product or selling patented technology to unauthorised person(s) will face life imprisonment, 10 lashes of the cane and a fine of $300,000.*

Standing in his office-bunk, no larger than a broom closet, Hayat tries not to think of the stone weighing in his bladder. He tries not to think of himself as the big bad wolf, staggering down to the river for a drink of water, a belly full of rocks. Little Red Riding Hood and her hunter-father hiding behind a tree, waiting for him to drown. So much fluid cruelty in one fairy tale. So much the ancients took for granted, coming back to mock the modern masses.

Hayat is going on holiday.

To be specific: Hayat is retiring. He will walk out of the State Guild's fascist architecture, its atrium filled with marble and gold, and book himself a coach-trip to the borderlands. He will take a first-class cabin on a rickety train, tearing up dust in the desert landscape. It will be like surfing on the moon. In his valise will be a toothbrush and a card made by his students wishing him happy travels: "We love you, Teacher Hayat Wee!"

He once dreamed of walking the empty bowls of the Indian Ocean and Dead Sea. These days, he only has mortality on his mind.

Also in his valise: his medication for prostate cancer.

There isn't much to look at, but Hayat takes a last look around his office bunk anyway.

Goodbye. Sod off, the room seems to breathe.

The agent who meets him at the border is dressed in white linen. A handsome man, with a line for a mouth and bedroom eyes. Hayat wants to put his finger gently into the man's dimple on his left cheek, but stops himself.

"Mr. Wee?"

Hayat takes the proffered hand and nods.

"The hotel's this way."

They walk in the dust, nothing but dust, in what used to be water surrounding the island state. All around them, people are striking out in all directions, the old and feeble straggling after the fit and able. They mill like zombies around the well-defended electric beaches of the guild. The have-waters and the have-nots.

The hotel stands on stilts. It must have been beautiful when the place was still an atoll. Luxury resort with azure waters and white sand. Fish wriggling between one's toes as one waded for miles out to sea. Now, its wood is rotting and the curtains are in tatters. Sun-bleached cushions and weathered steps between the chalets—whale-fall.

In the grotty room, overrun by cockroaches, the agent brushes the scorpions off a chair and sinks his ill-protected linen-covered bum on the flattened stuffing.

"Please," he says. Gestures with both hands at a chamber pot in the middle of the room.

Hayat looks into the pot's worn enamel bottom. As though it holds tea leaves that will help him divine his future. But he knows there is no future. The doctor's report had been very clear that it was Stage 4. Unless…

Hayat feels a sudden flash of anxiety. "$50 million. That's the agreed amount. Right?"

The agent's turn to nod. Raises an eyebrow. "Performance anxiety?"

"NO," says Hayat, louder than he intended.

But, yes, here he is, selling state secrets, portable kits smuggled in his valise with nano-syringes of purification solutions; little nets of reverse-osmosis filters hidden among his wet wipes.

Here he is, fed up with being a cog in the giant treatment wheel.

Here he is, taking a gamble, to hell with the consequences. The costly experimental treatment for his cancer, then the expensive business of staying alive on the run.

"Okay," he says.

The agent settles back in his chair again. To watch. Micturition, then testing. For turbidity, total hardness, total solid sulphates.

Total Trihalomethanes. After me, now. *Heterotrophic Plate Count*. Very good.

He will undress now. He will peel the DUNE suit off, emerging from it like a baby from a scab. He will be made fresh and new. Newer. He will stand for an eternity trying to let out a lifetime of recycled resentment. Of repression and injustice.

He will share his water with the rest of the world.

He will piss all over everybody who has kept him down.

As the cold air hits his skin, it occurs to him that he is losing moisture to the air. How much time left? How much moisture?

Whatever. A bell tinkers.

Old Water

Tamantha Smith

What stands between the girl and me is one last sip of water so old and feral, a water that quenched so many thirsts, it's more consuming than survival.

She's bones under a brittle hide. The last of her hair is gone, the beauty of cherub cheeks stilted with the emaciation of a young life grifting for water. She could be six years old, she could be ten, but her stunted growth keeps her looking eternally young, devastatingly younger.

Her parents are piled at her feet, dead or near-dead, no longer of use to her. I know that if she could cry, she would. But, for now, while her body cherishes every last drop of water, her grief remains etched in wide, sunken eyes and a half-slack jaw.

I stroke the flask, flash against my chest inside my coat. I feel the slosh and swirl of the last drop. Its power throbs, hitting against my own skeletal frame. Thinking of it rattles my bones. I've carried it for centuries, filled from the eternal fountain that gave youth to a motley crew of us; it gave us forever under the condition that we never drank from it twice.

I long for that second sip and the forever death it promises. I crave an exit from this desolate world where the less fortunate bleed to allow the more fortunate to live, and those in-between fortunes sit idly by.

The girl reminds me of someone: pools of brown eyes and a crooked nose, knobbly knees and webbed toes.

Don't make the connection, it'll only make the indecision harder.

The zombies I have made and left behind are unforgiveable. Little by little, I let the poor souls sip at the flask and gave them a life forever. We were all such fools, lusting for life when the real mercy was moving beyond. I check shadows now.

It's getting harder to tell the zombies from the dying—they're all dry bones, fighting the maggoty infestations coveting their survival. But the zombies have finally relinquished their hold on forever and know I have the last sip.

The girl is so small. She wants to live, it's all she's ever known, to live. She clings to the idea despite the lives flashing out around her, their parched bodies flaking into the dust of the drought-plagued soil. Her eyes stay open.

She opens her mouth in plea to stricken passers-by. They see her, they eye her, but they recognise the water in her is less than the effort they need to retrieve it, and they walk past.

I could walk past too. I could walk past into the forever, looking for the right time and the right place to forget about forever and down the last sip.

I don't walk past.

If I offer her this last sip, all we zombies are zombies forever. She too. Her tiny frame would walk in constant search of the fountain, long dried up as the water stopped. She would walk with memories too painful to forget and no hope of forgetting. As I do.

But we could walk together—broken souls, wedded together.

Before I think twice, before I remind myself of centuries of painful steps, I uncap the flask and hold it out to her.

She's not swift of thought, she doesn't trust easily, and she shouldn't.

A hand whips between us, all bones and taut skin like my own. I know this fast hand; it belongs to one of my zombies.

There's a split-second choice to make.

I down the last sip and watch as the girl picks up the fallen flask and licks at its spout.

Darkness—a new forever.

Handsome Fox Thirsts for More

Clare Rhoden

I

The dust rises, a dowdy red cloud of old souls. Nothing but the memory of life. Desiccated cells of plants and animals, soured now and then by the taint of dried human.

I don't like the way the red stuff cakes in the spaces between my toes, combines with the sweat from my pads and transforms into a dust-cast.

On the plus side, nobody and nothing can track me. All I leave behind are smudgy dents in the dust, and a time-delayed transmission for my mistress.

What more could a spy want?

II

Ma'am.

Greetings from your most humble servant. My on-the-ground observations, I know, are beamed to your Director of Hydration Projects via my transmitter collar. But I know of old how much you enjoy glimpses of life from your far-flung dependencies.

I thank you for your gracious comments on my last. It is true: a camera image cannot convey the situation completely.

I continue my trek down the east coast of the Great Southern Colony. The dust of this place is like nothing ever experienced at Home. It is somewhat like the powder formerly used in our kennels to deter pests (begging your pardon). Except that this powder is red and smells of charnel. It is not pleasant.

But I do not complain. Far from it, Ma'am. I am honoured to be your representative in these parts, and privileged to meet your honest servants at every staging post. My body is strong, my mind is keen, and my desire to serve you unswerving.

As predicted, few remain alive at each village, thus reducing the colony's need for hydration aid from abroad. All the large four-footed creatures have been expended, as have many of the humans, particularly those of lesser value. Birds are uncommon. Rabbits few. Rodents are even more rare, no doubt because there are no heaps of rubbish for them to inhabit. Everything is put to use—admirable efficiency, as you noted in your last.

These days one seldom sees any of the strange creatures that once entranced our forebears with their odd shapes and their ridiculous locomotions.

Fortunately, sufficient nourishment remains for your humble servant, who is greeted with courtesy and grace at each halt on his way south.

Yours in perpetuity
Sylvester

III

The next village is a miserable, bowl-shaped encampment that slouches like a badly wrought saucer between the degraded mounds that pass for mountains in this land. I know this place of old. Rain stopped falling here more than a decade ago, yet the altitude (such as it is) and the sere winds shred the demeaned hills to render the nights killingly cold.

I come here as much for the cold as for my mission. If I can find a skerrick of shelter to huddle through the darkest hours, then the dismal light of pre-dawn brings a bonus. Frost is not delicious, but lap it with a warm tongue and it's almost like drinking.

Of course, I compete with other creatures for this scarce resource, but they are mostly slow with cold and dull with hunger.

Cold and hunger act like a whetstone on the cogs of my mind. I feast. Marsupial mice and skinks don't have much blood, as it happens, but enough.

After breakfast, I trot round the barren dimple of the dry lakebed and take a turn about the marble halls of Par Le Mont house. I always found it laughable that this would-be grand building, huddled in this cheerless landscape of eroded hillocks, styles itself by the mountain. Amusements are scarcer than sheep these days, so I make the most of this one.

As the sun rises I enjoy a bask, leaning against the largest of the smooth stone columns in the roofless foyer, safe among the tumbled statues, tattered portraits and broken furniture. Riots have their uses. If not so open to the elements, this structure could accommodate fine dens. But freezing nights and burning days void promise of safety.

The servants of my mistress look up listlessly as I pass. I've long since relinquished hope for them. They have no power and they pay cursory attention to their assigned duties: keeping the peace, securing the sovereign's property, acting to preserve what life remains.

These goals make substantial check boxes that bear no relationship to the literal situation. I pity these humans. Let alone managing the remnant community, they have enough to do keeping themselves alive.

Which they mostly do by preying on each other, having learned that all the non-humans that survive thus far are much more clever than they are. But there have always been creatures more astute and pragmatic than humans.

I'm heading south in search of company. I cannot be the only fox remaining. As a species, we are well-equipped with our vigilant ways and inventive actions for most situations. A fox is rarely surprised, and even more rarely at a loss.

We are masters of wile, callous virtuosi. Some of us (ahem) are almost godlike in perceiving and then acting to our best advantage.

I see in my mind a future where foxkind dominates these plains.

The day of the human is over.

IV

Ma'am.

Greetings from your most humble servant.

I write in some haste and more trepidation. I must let you know that the last dregs of society in the Great Southern Colony have reached their limit. Their Ultima Thule, one might say, from which there is no returning.

A great many of your servants are no longer operative. Perished of the drought, the plague, the fires, or the hand of their fellows. The large populace which they guarded is now a mere skim of life on the dry facade that now covers the entire continent. Where once was an inland sea of exhausted soils and fragmented fossils, one now finds remarkably arty, but wholly natural, installations of bleached bones.

Ma'am, I implore you: send no more succour to this land. Save what clean water you have for Home. Freeze it if you may, to preserve its freshness for your future. On no account must charity ply the acid-steeped ocean that separates us. Save yourself. For me, Ma'am: save yourself so that I may die secure in your continued existence.

I write in pain, knowing I will never see your magnificence again. I beg you remember me kindly.

Yours eternally
Sylvester

V

It is done. My irksome transmitting collar is gone. I convinced a white-ribbed dingo to bite it from my neck, with a claim that it was torturing me.

All dogs are gullible. And quite palatable, compared to blue-tongued lizards.

No more sensors track my steps. No further reports flit Home via satellite. No more monitoring of one Sylvester Fox, late of Her Majesty's Service.

This is my time.

VI

A lucky sighting among the perished trees. A starved vixen ungainly with cub, the knobs of her spine more pronounced than the hills that count as mountains here.

I am handsome. I am eloquent. I am meek. I call her Ma'am and imagine I speak to my sovereign. The famished vixen likes the plan that I explain, most modestly. I will feed her, guard her, teach the cubs, make foxkind great again.

Her name is Missy. She does not know of what cubs I speak. These she carries now: they will feed us. The future of foxkind will have my genes.

I can wait.

VII

We prosper, Missy and I.

I surprise myself. I am more ingenious than I appreciated. Without the onerous transmitting collar, I find vigour and guile that surpass all my previous efforts. I am never at a loss. We eat well, if one considers the benefits of an insect diet.

My only complaint is that such fare is not juicy. But Missy has lost the hollow planes on her body, though one could not yet claim she is thriving. I look better, but then I do not carry a swag of young inside my ravenous body.

I am impatient for their arrival. They will be succulent.

VIII

Disaster.

Our way south is blocked by the churning grey width of an acid riverlet, so thick with ash and steeped in poison that the devastation of the land spreads for miles either side of it. Nothing lives, not even a fleck of sulphurous lichen.

We must find another route.

Missy claims more of our kind inhabit the slopes to the south of here. She should know: one of them fathered her brood.

I am keen to meet them, because all surviving local foxes stand in need of a great and educated leader.

IX

Joy.

Against all odds, and only because we turned away from what was once the major water source for these pathetic hillocks, we discover a valley. Perhaps more of a dell than a valley. A miniature basin of protection.

Missy sees it first: a drift of green among the tumbled granite. Hoping against hope for a mouthful of moss, we find instead a spring.

A spring! The tiniest welling of fresh water, one slow bubble at a time. But we call it The Spring, and here we den.

Only insects know this place. We sample spicy ants and slimy grubs, and at night we catch fat, greasy moths.

No meat ever tasted so good. In this ruined land, The Spring simulates an oasis. Missy intends to pup here.

She keeps to herself, but accepts any food I bring. Her attention is inward, her time very near.

Not long now till I feast; the vixen can please herself. Then we move south to find the rest of foxkind.

Next year's cubs will be mine.

X

I return to find her pacing, whining and anxious. The birthing begins, but I see now that Missy will fail. She has not the strength for this.

No great tragedy: her body will feed me even better than the two nut-sized, squirming balls of slime-slick fur that slip out of her.

Only two. I hoped for more. I give them a desultory lick to start them breathing. They taste—ah, so fresh.

They are deaf, blind, helpless. They will stay fresh for several hours.

Their dam, now, is another matter. All that blood, all that mess! She lies on her side, wheezing. Not strong enough to look at the litter.

I creep closer.

Her eye turns back in my direction. I see the white of it, stark and accusing. A shiver runs over me, like the dreadful tickle of my old transmitter collar, as though my life is not my own.

Enough. It must be now.
"Ma'am," I say, to put her at her ease.
She surges like a fanged tsunami.

XI

The vixen sits lightly panting by The Spring. Twins cubs gambol around her forepaws. Soon she will renew the trek south to rejoin her mate, stronger for her adventure.

The handsome fox was delicious. And meaty. His carcass fed them for almost a month.

She licks her lips, inspecting the new world.

Thick and Thin

Cheng Tim Tim

In Hong Kong, we say blood
is thicker than water, which is to say
our blood ties bond us, such
bonding, a given since birth,
undeniable, inescapable, the blood ties,
our basis for forgiveness,
forgiveness as our basis.

But what if this water
is our blood, the blood that trickles
and oozes colours from our bodies
as we cut ties, navigating
the pattern of our scar tissues
on our backs, our heads rugged
like barnacles carving themselves
onto stagnant, enclaved boats—
to end in clunks, power-washed
back to this brackish water,
this water as open

as our mind—Where does it stop
when we are led to think
that this water we drink every day
is not ours, it has to be sold and sent
through underground tunnels,
which we are led to think
as veins undeniable, inescapable,
under our daily fabric—

What to make of this water

around us, full of potential to be free
but instead is straightened,
stirred by the harsh, man-made shoreline
until it eels and japs, sending
the justice in droplets
into the thin air.

Water Syntax

Francesca Rendle-Short

/ˈwɔːtə/
absorb this, drink it (don't speak), just float the mashup (hydrobuoyed),

water (in English) from Old English *wæter* (as noun), *wæterian* (the verb),
boiling point 100 degrees
'moisten, irrigate, supply water to; lead (cattle) to water';
syntactical function: verb and mass noun
of Germanic origin, from Proto-Germanic *watar* (also of Old Saxon *watar*, Old Frisian *wetir*),
inorganic, transparent, tasteless, odourless
Dutch *water*, Old High German *wazzar*, German *Wasser*,
liquid aqua H-two-O loch pond bay pool lake river stream tributary pool ocean – sea
from an Indo-European root shared by Russian *voda* (compare with vodka),
aqueous hydrous liquid fluid
– wet wave current swell
Gothic 𐍅𐌰𐍄𐍉 (*wato*), Sanskrit *udrah*,
nearly colourless – damp moist sodden swampy miry – oooooozy
from Proto-Indo-European *wod-or*,
melting point 0 degrees
be in great plenty, Latin *abundare* 'overflow, run over',
the basis of all fluids of living organisms
suffixed form of root *wed-* ('water' or 'wet'),

sodium 5 mg, total fat 0 mg, calories 0
also Latin *unda* 'wave', Gaelic *uisge* 'water',
splash hose-down douse leak salivation wash
and Greek *hudōr* 'water',
partially dissociated into hydrogen and hydroxyl ions
the first (preserved Sanskrit *apah* as well as Punjab and julep) was animate',
sprinkle moisten dampen-spraysoaksinkdrownsoddendrenchsaturatewater-log – flood
Punjab etymologically 'the country of five waters', + *ab* 'water' from Iranian *ap-*,
with highly distinctive physical and chemical properties, it can dissolve many other
substances
related to rose water (*rhodon* and *rosa* and *roos*), sweet medicine,
one.of four elements in ancient and medieval philosophy and in astrology
'to dilute' attested from late 14c, now usually as *water down*
tears – cry – weep

Taking Turns

Stephen Embleton

"|Khupu-aos."

"Suckers of blood?"

"Very good," she attempted a smile and nodded slowly. "That is what they were called."

"We, Mama," corrected her daughter.

She sighed. "We are |Khupu-aos."

She wished it was different. She longed for the tales her grandmother had told her as her eyelids grew heavy. A little older than her own daughter was now, summer evenings after dinner spent with the family household huddled together in the living room. She would take her place, nestled against the old woman's warm chest, gently droning, soothing her, telling of a past and world unknown to her.

Nightfall shut off the desperate chaos of the outside world. Everyone into their houses, gathering their foodstuffs and prepping the small meals. Rationing. Stomachs reeling in protest at the fist-sized portions of !samma melon and murky cups of water, passed through the faltering filtration system.

Black water was deemed as safe as any water-source you could find in the surrounding area, reachable on foot if you had the stamina. But the !samma had steadily depleted, quicker than they could grow. Theft didn't help.

Amidst the rising conflicts, the matriarch had held everyone together with her tales of histories interweaved with the fantastical. Time, and cancers, slowly took its toll, her gruff tone becoming a wheeze as the eldest son, her father, would complete sentences. Waves of illnesses moved through the village and the homes, severing friends and acquaintances away from families to form untrusting huddles, weary of anyone coming too close.

Angry voices of adults in the house disturbed one fever-filled dream. She had dragged herself to the doorway to listen. Rumours of an exodus. Hints of betrayals. But her grandmother had been resolute in leaving the outside village to its own devices. *Blood comes first!*

She remembered clearly one evening, her uncle had whispered of the talk among the neighbours filtering in from afar, of the desperate need to find a solution to the lack of water.

The |ao|gomses would come to the houses, to leech the blood from you, leeching to cure and remove the badness. They performed their rites, burned their herbs and sucked the wounds. They talked of cleansing and healing the land, person by person, providing their ancient hope and interpretations.

Weeks and months later, no one could recall where they heard it first. But they understood of the nourishment present here, in this liquid, in this bowl, in her hands. This was nothing near medicinal. This was survival at a cost. The idea had assimilated. But not for everyone in the house.

"I am no |khupu-aob," her grandmother had hissed and spluttered.

A chill ran through her as she traced the trajectory of those words that late night, of how a single conversation revolving around science and reasoning, facts and justifications had led to this very moment.

Her face flushed. Her stomach ached.

And yet her senses, her sight and smell, screamed otherwise. The ringing in her ears, her ancestors? The ringing in her ears, a terrified, petrified heart? Her senses screamed, *no!*

Instinct arose and every fibre of her body said, this sight, this smell, this substance, should not be here. It should not be here in any quantity. For it to be here means something must be dead or dying. And yet to her touch, the warm pulse of her hands around the bowl said this was warm. This was nourishment.

The death she held in her hand was life.

She caught herself, startled at the vivid memories of her childhood, as if jolted awake from her grandmother's bosom.

Her daughter looked up at her, wide-eyed and waiting, unaware of the depths her memories had dragged her to. Only they remained from a family ravaged.

The copper bowl felt warmer than it had when the blood was leaking into it minutes before. It felt alive. She could not shake the sensation. She told herself it was only her own pulse coursing blood through her palms and fingers that she was feeling. The blood bowl was dead. Unfeeling. It was keeping her alive.

"|Khupu-aob", she whispered. That was who she had become.

She wanted a straw. A filtration straw. Anything but the direct taste, the slippery smooth liquid, the coppery aftertaste in her mouth and throat. Her mother had been the first one to rummage through the piles of straws bundled into recycling bags, never put out for collection and never collected. Reused until clogged and unusable.

Would those devices of her youth even work on blood? She wished they would.

The loud people had come, speakers blaring, with boxes and crates of filtration straws. Truckloads of good intentions they later realised, assumed, meant they would consume less from their water table. *Why truck in pumps and tankers when we can give them some straws for a few months? Recycle. Reuse. Survive.*

She wasn't looking forward to the dry rooibos branch she would need to gnaw on, hopefully countering the burst of iron to her system.

The sound of her daughter smacking her lips sent a pang of guilt into her gut.

She wished she'd learned the rites of a |ao|gomseb. She wanted it clean. She wanted herself to be cleaned, of the guilt and the shame.

The girl chewed, open-mouthed, eyes fixed on her mother while a finger unconsciously prodded the gauze plaster on her arm. Strips of the bitter-tasting !khoba succulent suppressed the appetite so that tonight she, the parent, could feed. Feed off her child.

She could not get past the rotten-smelling plant causing an uncontrollable gag. Bile filled her throat but she swallowed hard.

She returned her gaze to the bowl of her daughter's blood. The thought of rooibos did not seem too bad right then.

Her feelings were mixed, conflicting: regret at using her child, but ultimately it was the envy that trumped all. Envy that her child, any child, could not survive even small blood losses, where an adult could. She could always give her daughter more of herself than she, in turn, could take.

And the child would happily take it all. The growing body demanded it.

"It's okay, Mama." For a moment her daughter's kind words reassured her. "It's my turn tomorrow."

Thingo

Nicki Bacon

Stare at me from a distance,
A tale of boredom now known.
Stare at me from a closeness,
My life, a dullness sewn.

This flash of light is but a journey,
Some hundred-year sorrow.
So far from a fairy tale,
Oh, how I dread the morrow.

Told of such independence,
I'm forever alone.
I've flatlined and atoned,
Yet here merely groan.

Is this my torment?
A twisted prison devoid.
Through pain I persist,
Forsaken yet paranoid.

When the Water Drips

Seb Doubinsky

(Non-haikus)

all our wealth
contained within
these cupped hands

***

this woman
like a dry log
ready to burn
but giving no heat

***

no one is guilty
no one is innocent
judgement of nature
has no scales

***

profit measured
by water
profit measured
by bones

***

I speak

but my tongue is thick
words dry up
before spoken

***

sometimes I dream of water
it's always a happy dream
among the vastness of sand

***

when the water drips
time stands still
we stand still

when there are no more water-drops

Pandora

(Translated from Burmese to English by Kè Su Thar)

is there no more tie now
just like the circulation of water stops
and no more water-drops?
when doting on, we do dote passionately.
when hating, we do hate absolutely,
just as a withered branch crackles.

"if there is no water, drink oil,"
a wealthy woman slips out.
the water-searching drove,
rolling their tongues,
turning their heads toward
where the saliva she spits in disgust scatters.

"if there's no water,
people can't learn how to swim,
and they will drown to death,"
the ridiculous joke no-one remembers.
thirsty guys,
whenever they see the bulging veins of the skinny,
they dribble.
out of every pore of dry skin,
a soul struggles to rise.

water, water, water water everywhere.

water water everything is water.
water in flesh and bone. water in peace dialogue.
water is medicine. water, nutrition. water, love. water, weapon.
water fills the sky, yet it rains selectively in some places.
water overfills the sea, and it spills over beach-
salty water undrinkable.
water is put into man-made, exquisite bottles of priced-
purified water.
clear drops of water are gone.
things the water filter leaves behind are just
the bad ripples of memories, but
how can we cut, kill the water?
with what can we draw borderlines on the water?
to the days we struggled to reach water painstakingly,
to the ones who lost water at the most arid times,
the meaning of water on the opposite bank will swim back again.

Note:

In Burmese culture, 'water-drop" refers to 'ties which people had knotted in their previous lives'.

Downpour

E. Don Harpe

Ten-year-old Maggie Johnson stood in her front yard, starin' at de purple clouds rollin' in from de Northeast. She seemed excited but, wit Maggie, it were hard to tell. Like lots o' chillun, most o' de time Lil Maggie gots ants in her pants anyways. Couldn't stand still one jiffy.

"Looks lak rain," she said, to nobody in particular. "Yessir, I believes it's a'goin' to pour down most any minute."

Ole man Gilbert, he were standin' beside her, havin' stepped off his porch a few minutes afore Maggie come out of her house.

"Nope, dat jist somethin' yore wishin' fer, chile, not somethin' dat has any chance of really happenin'."

"Why not, Mr. Gilbert," Maggie wanted to know, "why ain't we gots no rain in over a year now?"

"Best I kin tell, chile, dem scientist fellers up in Washington been playin' wit da weather 'n all, shootin' dem signals up in de air, tryin' to stop de hurricanes. Well, dey sho nuff stopped 'em."

"Stopped de hurricanes, Mr. Gilbert?"

"Yeah, Lil Maggie, dey stopped de hurricanes. Trouble is, dey stopped everything else too. Stopped de thunder and de lightning, 'cept fer a hard strike ever now and den, which I could do without. Dey stopped all de water from fallin'.' I dunno if we is ever goin' to get any more rain."

"Wut we goin't do 'bout it, Mr. Gilbert? Ain't dey nothin' we kin do?"

"Well, 'bout all we kin do is pray, Lil Maggie, jist pray I reckon. Dat's 'bout all dat pore folks kin do 'bout anythin'. Jist pray."

"Will de prayers start de rain back up, Mr. Gilbert?" Maggie looked serious, concerned, her face still turned to de clouds.

"Naw, chile, all our prayers, dey gonna do da same thing dey always has. Nothin'. A big fat nothin'."

"Den why do we pray, Mr. Gilbert?"

"Because dat's all pore folks kin do, Lil Maggie. Shut our eyes and pray to some God somewhere out dere on de other side o' de sky, dat we ain't never seen a'tall. But he ain't listenin'."

"No, Mr. Gilbert?"

"No sir, Lil Maggie, He ain't, never has been. I been prayin' to him since't I t'were yer age, and he ain't never answered nary a one. Not a single prayer 'o mine did he even one time consider fer answerin'."

"Well, Mr. Gilbert, I 'spect de ole God will hear my prayer. How can he not listen to a chile over somethin' as important as water?"

"All's yew kin do is try, Lil Maggie. Jist close yore eyes and give her yer best shot."

Maggie closed her eyes. "Mister God, we needs some rain here today, lest we is gonna jist naturally die from vein' so thirsty." For emphasis, she stamped her foot hard on the dry cracked ground.

Mr. Gilbert, he just chuckled.

But about dat time a lil sparrow lit on a low hangin' branch in de ancient live oak tree above Maggie's head. Wit a cheerful peep, de bird let go a single drop o' poop, which struck Lil Maggie directly on her upturned forehead.

Maggie opened her eyes and began dancin' around Mr. Gilbert, squealin' wit unfettered joy. She paused for a moment and wiped a dirty hand across her forehead, removin' most of de bird poop.

"Well, Mr. Gilbert," she said, her voice filled with what passed for awe in a 10-year-old. "I 'spect yore wrong dis time. I jist wiped off a drop o' rain. Mr. God did answer my prayer."

Ole man Gilbert, he pulled a white kerchief from his pocket and gently wiped away de remainder o' de sparrow poop.

"Danged right, Lil Maggie," he smiled. "I s'ppose he did at dat." He took her hand in a mist fatherly fashion.

"Now c'mon chile, let's go on back in de house. We don't wants to get soaked in de downpour, now do we?"

"No, sir," Lil Maggie chirped to his smile.

a near-perfect picture

Eugen Bacon

my gasps dry. ancient eyes,
broken lips, a crumble of teeth
punctuate this webbed face. sub-
terranean lives, sluiced metaphors.
languages too slippery to know.
where's my innocence so you can
trust it. you sully its enthusiasm,
you leader of the nation, oh, rich
woman in the metropolis. the dark
presses with new lexes,
unpunctuated pasts simpering
way after i'm gone.
i am nameless in the edgelands
whose only maps are
goggle-eyed cockles
from a suspicious owl.
shiver. cut me a hole.
no one is coming.
seconds to midnight.
mercy.

Sifting Questions

Eugen Bacon

She rehearses the chat she'll have tomorrow as the climate turns. Paths cut all the way down hardened seas, parched trails stencilled with desert ants, concrete fish in odd numbers out of context, but so is the wisp of greyed hair on the nape of her neck. Wind nags, steals moisture that is an absence on a palimpsest poem long faded—how to scrape it from her brow? It feels unfair but less deadly to scrawl on stoned—as in golem not sozzled—tilapia

that breathes the same drought
and exhales different.
It's a timeless story
passing years over painted
water full of minuses
no more bleeds
what good is it
when she's drowning
on crimson dust?

The Chorus for Water

Ramya Jirasinghe

We are, we are, the people you don't want to see
Those who stand outside your gates
We are the ones who seek you day and night
We will haunt your dinner and midnight dreams
You thrive on the blood you sucked from our veins
You feed your children on our dried bones
You play games in the water that we wait for
To flood our souls and drench our cracked tongues
We are, we are, the people you cannot face
Look at us. Look at us. Look us in the eye
Tell us you can sleep at night if you
Look at us, look at us, look at us.

We are the ghosts of the living murdered
Those you have buried in their thirst
Those burnt in your bonfires of denial
We are the ghosts that crawl down your spine
When you sit awake at night searching for dreams.
We are the voices that fill your ears
Shouting for you to look over the sound of your fountains
We are the debris under your feet, the bones that you crush
We are the ghosts of the living killed by the
Weight of your jokes and long deliberations

One day, you will meet us on your last journey
Then you can tell us what you see in our eyes.
Look at us until you drown.
Drown drown drown.

Where (x) (is) Why Diary: Jeju Island Fragments

Kyongmi Park
(Translated by Jill Jones and Rina Kikuchi)

Into the sea's depths
the body sinking is my own

—

From this point there's not knowing
which becomes unknowing

not being able to hear
not being able to listen

then

now

—

this sinking self
is watching

as I sink

—

and there's this delicate algae
as if bubbles

are brushing my skin

stroking me gently
in soft turmoil round my ears

—

So
we know how this
rippling
breathes itself into words
begins talking

The soft imprint of words
fizzes on the skin
thinks onto the skin

—

Each bubble
boils as ferment
effervescing up

as words
faintly, quietly
blurring into the mirage
blending, shivering
into low colours of dusk

–

See
the water's so wide

a sea trying to drown me
a sky my family belongs to

They shimmer so far

If I try to stretch my arms out
Just once!
From sea deep to sky deep

—

The hospital room fills with soft afternoon light. The white curtain blurs as it absorbs the off-white glow of the sun's rays.

Such a relief, that all this falling white light deflects and softens. As if melting the hardness of those who come into the room, those ones whose steps drag such harshness in here, like a pollution.

A bleach smell hangs in the air, and our noses. The walls corral all this whiteness.

And there she is, as if comatose, as if sleeping, covered in a white quilt. That one, whose closed eyes and silvery hair seem to hide what might have been abundant.

That one, whose hair is still supple and elegant, whose hair weaves and billows around her head like a vine withering, but also gathered, also reserved.

That one, who's the eldest sister of my father, whose hair floats around her like seaweed.

—

Colours merge in you
disappear inside you

hidden by a mother's shawl
a grandmother's mask
layers wrapped in layers

—

I'm one of the knots
yet so small in this wrapping

I tear apart some of this wrapping
gnaw on fragments
knot them together again
sucking in the warmth of saliva
the sweet soapy smell of breast milk

I chew over these things, fretting
not wanting to let go
but the smell, the taste of it
has been so long with me
I gnaw and I gnaw

—

That one opens her eyes, just barely.

'Ah, I'm sleeping. As it always seems to be, now. But it's not yet evening. No, not yet.' As though deep wrinkles around those eyes can talk, those eyes that almost look like they've given up everything. But this has also played out before. Those eyes open, just barely. As though this one knows someone's there.

Those eyes have become so vivid in a way I'd never have thought possible – such a change, such a hue. This one's strong will lies in the depths of her pupils. That fire of dwindling life still strong in this one.

I feel my own fire – it's both the urgency of burning tears and a frozen deep core.

'Sister, elder sister.' My mother speaks to her, this elder sister, crouching next to the white bed.

'Aunty!' I'm still standing. I'm that person who half-says this word.

My mother, filled with emotion, bows deeply before the cold eyes of her sister. And I watch every movement of my aunt. I'm trying to put so much distance between me and all the last remainder of this old fire.

—

As I sank into the ocean
I wondered how many minutes there were
left in this, my last diving time

How much did I seize?
Oh yes, I was never beaten
at abalone catching!

I don't know how
I drowned in
this last sinking

This was
the last
Yes, the last!

All that greed!
Yes, I needed to stay in the water
as long as I could

This last dive
was my fate, a fate
of a long line of women

That deep tempest
seething
boiling up and over

Do you know
how much
that old spirit churns?

I only just found out
how it gushes up
around me now

As though I'm still living
while I'm dying
dying while I'm still living

Because of all this
endless bubbling
boiling, gushing, swelling

Words gush up
to make this
poem

Words reach up
boiling, babbling, jabbering
over and over and over

Bodysurfing

Dominique Hecq

Broken crane on the waterline. The scent of cut grass. A pong of fish wiping out sand, sea breeze and trimmed lawns. Dead mussels glare along the shore. Seagulls peck and caw at the air. The beach sunshine cuts through me. My stomach gurgles. I shift my hunger to my son's pale body. Ask whether he's applied sunscreen. No answer. I watch as he wades in. So used to watching, as is the lifeguard—radio crackling at his hip, whistle between his lips. He embodies the authority I long lost. His relentless gaze and taut muscles inspire trust. I run into the waves towards my Ahron. Cold slap of water on sizzling skin. Salt. I leap with joy, a fiction in time to a breaker's smack. Salt on my lips. On my tongue. Throat burns. Soon I can't breathe for all that salt and water. I try raising my hand. Breakers slap my face. In a flash I remember telling all my children but one never to dive into unfamiliar waters. I cough, splutter, choke, drool. Utter an incoherent word. Shut the fuck up, says my grown son. My eyes have lost sight of the life-guard. And the line where the water stops. Whack! My head bobs up and down. Stomach fills with water. Arms and legs want to crawl back to shore, but currents push them back again and again. As if you could predict everything from the beginning, I hear a voice climbing from deep in my sore gullet: rrrhhelp!

When the Water Stops (Cantonese)

Cheng Tim Tim & Zephyr Li

無水

(Cantonese version of 'When the Water Stops')

隨著氣候轉變，大自然投下山火，將屋仔燒成白地，沙塵暴吹散無數家庭，大旱——所有牛羊都無曬，得返層皮，死剩排骨。喘喘開始個陣，村民輪流輸血，分擔夢想同恐懼，佢哋明白作為一個人，大家都係**咁**高**咁**大。

但一個正常**嘅**成年男性只有五公升血——無四成就已經死得。可以捐**嘅39%**血裏面，得**92%**係佢哋需要**嘅**水，其餘**嘅**浪費咗喺葡萄糖、激素、蛋白質、脂肪、維他命，礦物鹽同二**氧**化**碳**到——**咁**好咩？二**氧**化**碳**會令人頭暈、疲倦、煩躁不安、抽**搐**或昏迷。考慮到所有**嘅**缺點，條村輪流輸血，最後會剩幾多水？

佢哋仔細考慮呢個問題嗰陣，志願者繼續為部落輸血，之後就用四到八星期**嘅**時間吸吮仙人掌葉、樹液、無花果同沙漠螞蟻。但係佢哋嘅體力仍然唔能夠喺下一次輸血**嘅**時候恢復。損失**嘅**嘢係無法補回。

所以，佢哋由最初**嘅**自願參加，變到而家**嘅**抽籤決定——一係好彩、一係唔好彩； 長籤就係長籤，短籤就係短籤。如果**你**抽到短**嘅**，**你**就係**咁歹**，**你**唯一**嘅**安慰就係，呢種死亡並唔孤獨，反而係滿足社群需要**嘅**融合。

但抽籤最後都停止咗。犧牲太大。所以而家屠殺**嘅**決定就落入有錢人，或者有多啲武力**嘅**人手上。打個比喻，邊個**嘅**骨灰可以漂浮喺空中都係佢哋話哂事。一切都發生喺甕缸入邊。

甕缸入邊嘅女人

係熱浪之下，佢成個星期都坐咗喺個碗度。佢俾回憶所淹沒，令人昏睡**嘅**回憶正以慢鏡重播。當佢以後**諗**起呢刻，佢又會記起啲乜？佢望住盤旋緊**嘅**煙，啲煙就好似一個仁慈**嘅**擁抱，巨雲再冒出幾個字：**你**身在何方？佢**嘅**靈魂係天空中最光亮**嘅**。今日，佢係輸血者。聽日係一個盼望。

國家領袖

十年前，大領袖離開咗佢嘅庇護所，決心佔領變為教宗博物館**嘅**聖殿臺階。佢嘴藐藐噉高舉聖經整整一分鐘，嚇到班人權領袖、幾個高院法官同無數阿媽呆咗。裝備住警棍、橡膠子彈同防毒面具**嘅**防暴警察，壓咗落揮動「愛與珍惜**嘅**藝術」口號**嘅**和平示威者身上。

當經濟重要過社會動盪而股票又升到叭叭聲時，一滴血算得啲乜？**你**唔見道指升咗267點咩？仲有納指**嘅**上升？進化論就係講物競天擇，邊種模式能夠保留最多仿效者就可以生存。

光年之外，平行宇宙**嘅**每個大主教都對敬拜設施被亂用而震怒，再**諗**起自古以來對人道原則**嘅**違反，佢哋頓咗五個字出**嚟**：我。㖞。唔。到。氣。

抗爭永遠都係**咁**嘈喳，領袖心**諗**。新選舉又近喇。

都市入邊嘅富婆

「水停咗，血就要不停流」，手腕戴住手鈪形彩虹鑽石**嘅**女人噉講。呢套價值億億聲**嘅**心口針連極光吊墜套裝，係由一個叔公個姪**嘅**姪送**嘅**禮物。但女人點都**諗**唔起佢個名，太難喇。

女人食低下階層**嘅**人血饅頭起家，就好似係佢地牢裏面**嚟**自村莊**嘅**乞兒。女人唔信美術史學家啲舊相所反映**嘅**故事。女人**嘅**思維正正造就咗希特拉、墨索里尼同伊迪. 阿敏。女人對唔屬於近乎完美**嘅**人無哂辦法，每次見到呢啲人，就好似面對錯誤、令人尷尬**嘅**回憶，覺得佢哋次次都形象唔同，無樣係真。有關人性**嘅**書好多，但實在太難喇！

「叫嗲啦！」女人孖叉佢啲工人。呻吟並唔係由黑鍵白鍵所發出**嘅**聲音，唔會跟從主旋律演奏。如果佢哋嘅哀嚎係詰問，噉佢哋嘅哀嚎就係巴別塔中**嘅**一種語言。女人唔明白當中**嘅**聲韻、音節、句法、寓意或語境，亦都無可能去嘗試。實在太難**啦**！

有**乜**唔難理解呢？就係擁有獨特芳香的優質年**份**佳釀。由條村直送、價錢相宜兼血體純正，未受城市污染。條村**嘅**血恰到揉合酸度同甘甜**嘅**煙燻味，略帶煙肉、黑椒，最後以紫羅蘭及銅味收結。

為咗佢嘅種族得以存活，優質**嘅**血必須不斷流落去。女人深情**咁**將隻拉布拉多貴婦狗抱到心口。

受壓村夫

當佢開始搵原因時，翻天覆地嘅改變已經殺到嚟。

呢個「原因」源自要用三塊木薯餅塞飽十四把口嘅現實；呢個「原因」逼到佢問：要嬶定要仔女？老婆將仔女帶嚟世界；仔女令佢墜入無間折磨。

或者呢個只係佢變得殘忍嘅藉口，以宣洩每日嘅仇恨、怨憤同後悔恨……呢啲情緒好似侏狨噉潛入嚟再滋生成害蟲：偷嘢、老爆、諸如此類。佢唔係個種會係慘痛婚姻中怨天怨地嘅人，可以話係恐懼左右咗佢哋決定。假如佢老婆嘅翻天覆地改變殺到嚟，毫無疑問佢都要面對現實：要隻佬定要仔女？

老公就噉做咗，無錯。唔好意思。人哋話甕缸入邊嘅事發生得好快。

佢當然有掛住有人聽佢呻嘅日子。但宜家佢夠錢餵飽啲細路，最細嗰個仲要得兩歲。Afia，星期五出世；Abimbola，含住金鎖匙出世但一直做窮人；Amara，曾經優雅但宜家嚴重缺乏蛋白質而肚大頭禿；Chi、Ke、Re、Po，頭髮枯旱眼裏有沙嘅四胞胎。

佢做咗，因為老婆之後……仲有十四個選擇。

Afia，十四個喪母子女中排行第五嗰個

我係爛溶溶路上**嘅**碎蛋；我係刀片鐵絲網上垂死**嘅**雀仔。隻豺狼**踱嚟踱**去，度緊點樣食咗我。我又開始念舊喇，無學校、無湯，只有空洞**嘅**天喺我哋自我埋葬時呼嘯；我係被標記**嘅**卡——一點紅。支箭會呼一聲直插乾涸**嘅**泉眼。**你**係**咪**我媽**咪**？有副**骷**髏骨被黑曼巴蛇**嘅**嘶嘶聲困住。灰色羽毛以錯**嘅**方式旋轉。

最細嗰個話

我**搵**緊一啲我都唔知係**乜嘅**嘢。有手同目光、笑容同香味。係一種舒適，一**份**溫暖；我唔記得**嚟**完又去**嘅**樣、有裂痕**嘅**愛。係複雜，亦唔安全，模糊而佈滿碎屑。

念舊，一個**拎**住空袋**嘅**叔公，臭丸味**嘅**口氣，佢**嘅**眼睛係針對希望**嘅**要塞。**你諗**起呢刻，一次又一次，但願**你**同所有人都可以記得唔一樣**嘅**世界。

When the Water Stops / 無水

AS THE CLIMATE turned, it hurled at them bushfires that razed huts to the ground, dust storms that swept away families, drought – all the cattle and sheep gone, reduced to skin, then skeletons. At first, the villagers took turns on the bleed, sharing dreams and fears, understanding that as a people they were the same.

隨著氣候轉變，大自然投下山火，將屋仔燒成白地，沙塵暴吹散無數家庭，大旱——所有牛羊都無曬，得返層皮，死剩排骨。啱啱開始個陣，村民輪流輸血，分擔夢想同恐懼，佢哋明白作為一個人，大家都係**咁**高**咁**大。

But a typical grown male has a blood volume of just five litres – a forty per cent loss is deadly. The threshold thirty-nine per cent has only ninety-two per cent water in it; the rest is washed away in glucose, hormones, proteins, fats, vitamins, mineral salts and carbon dioxide – what good is it? $C0_2$ may induce dizziness, tiredness, restlessness, convulsions or coma. So, given all the minuses, how much water would be left from a bleed to go around a village?

但一個正常**嘅**成年男性只有五公升血——無四成就已經死得。可以捐**嘅39%**血裏面，得**92%**係佢哋需要**嘅**水，其餘**嘅**浪費咗喺葡萄糖、激素、蛋白質、脂肪、維他命，礦物鹽同二**氧**化**碳**到——**咁**好咩？二**氧**化**碳**會令人頭暈、疲倦、煩躁不安、抽**搐**或昏迷。考慮到所有**嘅**缺點，條村輪流輸血，最後會剩幾多水？

They sifted the question in their minds while volunteers, having bled for the clan, sucked on cactus leaves and sap, figs and desert ants for four to eight weeks afterward. But still they were not strong enough to take another turn when it arrived. The loss was not replenished.

佢哋仔細考慮呢個問題嗰陣，志願者繼續為部落輸血，之後就用四到八星期**嘅**時間吸吮仙人掌葉、樹液、無花果同沙漠螞蟻。但係佢哋嘅體力仍然唔能夠喺下一次輸血**嘅**時候恢復。損失**嘅**嘢係無法補回。

So where first they volunteered, now they drew sticks – it was plain luck, or missed luck. A stick was a stick, a short one was short. If you drew it, your fate was sealed, your only solace that this death would not be a lonely one, but rather a communion that met society's needs.

所以，佢哋由最初**嘅**自願參加，變到而家**嘅**抽籤決定——一係好彩、一係唔好彩； 長籤就係長籤，短籤就係短籤。如果**你**抽到短**嘅**，**你**就係**咁**歹，**你**唯一**嘅**安慰就係，呢種死亡並唔孤獨，反而係滿足社群需要**嘅**融合。

But even the drawing of sticks stopped eventually. It was a sacrifice too big. So now it was a matter for those with money, or bigger sticks, to determine who to massacre. And that determined whose ashes would float in the air, figuratively speaking. What really happened took place in the vat.

但抽籤最後都停止咗。犧牲太大。所以而家屠殺嘅決定就落入有錢人，或者有多啲武力嘅人手上。打個比喻，邊個嘅骨灰可以漂浮喺空中都係佢哋話晒事。一切都發生喺甕缸入邊。

The woman in the vat
甕缸入邊嘅女人

What she's doing this week is sitting in a bowl, right there in the heat shimmer. She's awash with memories of drowsing, unfolding, everything in slow motion. When she looks back on this time, what will she remember? She watches the smoke swirling like a benevolent hug, giant clouds bubbling out the words: *Where are you now?* Her soul is an object brightest in the sky. Today, she's a bleed. Tomorrow is a wish.

係熱浪之下，佢成個星期都坐咗喺個碗度。佢俾回憶所淹沒，令人昏睡嘅回憶正以慢鏡重播。當佢以後諗起呢刻，佢又會記起啲乜？佢望住盤旋緊嘅煙，啲煙就好似一個仁慈嘅擁抱，巨雲再冒出幾個字：你身在何方？佢嘅靈魂係天空中最光亮嘅。今日，佢係輸血者。聽日係一個盼望。

The leader of the nation
國家領袖

Ten years ago, the big leader came out of his shelter, determined to occupy the steps of a shrine opened as a museum to the Pope. He stunned human rights leaders, a few high courts and many mothers when he pushed out his lip and held up a Bible for one full minute as cameras snapped. Riot police fell with batons, rubber bullets and gas masks on peaceful protesters brandishing slogans about the art of cherishing and love.

十年前，大領袖離開咗佢嘅庇護所，決心佔領變為教宗博物館嘅聖殿臺階。佢嘴藐藐噉高舉聖經整整一分鐘，嚇到班人權領袖、幾個高院法官同無數阿媽呆咗。裝備住警棍、橡膠子彈同防毒面具嘅防暴警察，壓咗落揮動「愛與珍惜嘅藝術」口號嘅和平示威者身上。

What was a drop of blood when the economy outweighed civil unrest and stocks soared higher? Did you see the Dow, a gain of 267 points?

And the advances in the Nasdaq Composite? Evolutionary theory was all about natural selection of the form that would leave the most copies of itself.

當經濟重要過社會動盪而股票又升到叭叭聲時，一滴血算得啲乜？你唔見道指升咗267點咩？仲有納指嘅上升？進化論就係講物競天擇，邊種模式能夠保留最多仿效者就可以生存。

Light-years on, every archbishop in an alternate universe, outraged by the misuse of a facility of worship, would consider the historic violation of the principles of humanity and utter three spaced words: I. Can't. Breathe.

光年之外，平行宇宙嘅每個大主教都對敬拜設施被亂用而震怒，再諗起自古以來對人道原則嘅違反，佢哋頓咗五個字出嚟：我。唞。唔。到。氣。

Protests were always ugly, thought the leader. And a new election was coming up.

抗爭永遠都係咁嘜喳，領袖心諗。新選舉又近喇。

The rich woman in the metropolis
都市入邊嘅富婆

When the water stops, the blood must flow, says the woman with a rainbow diamond shaped into a bangle around her wrist. The billion-dollar brooch – a set with an aurora pendant – was a gift from a cousin of a cousin of a great-uncle whose name she tried to remember but couldn't. It was just too hard.

「水停咗，血就要不停流」，手腕戴住手鈪形彩虹鑽石嘅女人噉講。呢套價值億億聲嘅心口針連極光吊墜套裝，係由一個叔公個姪嘅姪送嘅禮物。但女人點都諗唔起佢個名，太難喇。

She flourishes from the catastrophe of others. Blooms on the unimportant. Like the people in her cellar, beggars from the village. Theirs is a narrative she doesn't believe in, the kind of story reflected in old photos by art historians. Her fabric is the politics that gave rise to Hitler, Mussolini and Idi Amin Dada. She can't help it if those people don't belong in a near-perfect picture. They are mistakes, awkward memories that float a different image every time she looks, never authentic. There are many books about humanity, but this is hard!

女人食低下階層嘅人血饅頭起家，就好似係佢地牢裏面嚟自村莊嘅乞兒。女人唔信美術史學家啲舊相所反映嘅故事。女人嘅思維正正造就咗希特拉、墨索里尼同伊迪．阿敏。女人對唔屬於近乎完美嘅人無哂辦法，每次見到呢啲人，就好似面對錯誤、令人尷尬嘅回憶，覺得佢哋次次都形象唔同，無樣係真。有關人性嘅書好多，但實在太難喇！

Turn off the sound of their groaning! she snaps to her servants. The moaning is a sound that's never black or white. It doesn't obey the rules of composition. If their cry is a question, it's a cry in a language of Babel. She doesn't understand its vowels, syllables, syntax, parables or context, and it's impossible to try. Because that's so hard!

「叫嗲啦！」女人孖叉佢啲工人。呻吟並唔係由黑鍵白鍵所發出嘅聲音，唔會跟從主旋律演奏。如果佢哋嘅哀嚎係詰問，噉佢哋嘅哀嚎就係巴別塔中嘅一種語言。女人唔明白當中嘅聲韻、音節、句法、寓意或語境，亦都無可能去嘗試。實在太難啦！

What's not hard to understand is vintage produce with a good nose. The ones from the village come at a good price and their blood is pure, uncontaminated by the city's pollution. Village blood combines the right acidity with a sweet aroma of smoke. Bacon and pepper, violets inside a copper finish.

有乜唔難理解呢？就係擁有獨特芳香的優質年份佳釀。由條村直送、價錢相宜兼血體純正，未受城市污染。條村嘅血恰到揉合酸度同甘甜**嘅**煙燻味，略帶煙肉、黑椒，最後以紫羅蘭及銅味收結。

And vintage blood must flow for the survival of her species. She cradles with affection a labradoodle puppy to her breast.

為佢佢嘅種族得以存活，優質**嘅**血必須不斷流落去。女人深情**咁**將隻拉布拉多貴婦狗抱到心口。

A village husband under pressure
受壓村夫

The revolution came when he alluded to reason.

當佢開始**搵**原因時，翻天覆地**嘅**改變已經殺到**嚟**。

It was a reason created from the reflection of fourteen hungry mouths and three dry cassava biscuits to go around. It was a reason that made him ask the question: wife or children? She'd brought them into existence. They initiated a cycle of living that was a torment.

呢個「原因」源自要用三塊木薯餅塞飽十四把口嘅現實；呢個「原因」逼到佢問：要媽定要仔女？老婆將仔女帶嚟世界；仔女令佢墜入無間折磨。

Perhaps his was an excuse to be unkind, to give voice to everyday hatreds, resentments, regrets . . . They crept in like dwarf monkeys and grew into pests: stealing, raiding, and all that. He was not the sort of person to hold a grudge on matters that came along with a sad marriage, so it was right to say it was fear that decided his choice. When his wife's own revolution came, there was no question where her truth lay: husband or children?

或者呢個只係佢變得殘忍**嘅**藉口，以宣洩每日**嘅**仇恨、怨憤同後悔恨……呢啲情緒好似侏狨噉潛入**嚟**再滋生成害蟲：偷嘢、老爆、諸如此類。佢唔係個種會係慘痛婚姻中怨天怨地**嘅**人，可以話係恐懼左右咗佢哋決定。假如佢老婆**嘅**翻天覆地改變殺到**嚟**，毫無疑問佢都要面對現實：要隻**佬**定要仔女？

He made things happen, yeah. Sorry. They said what happened in a vat was quick.
老公就噉做咗，無錯。唔好意思。人哋話甕缸入邊**嘅**事發生得好快。

He did miss having someone to rant to. But there was enough money to feed hungry children now, the youngest just two. Afia, the Friday-born child. Abimbola, the rich-born child but always poor. Amara, the graceful one now potbellied and bald with kwashiorkor. Chi, Ke, Re, Po, the quadruplets with nylon hair and eyes filled with sand.

佢當然有掛住有人聽佢呻**嘅**日子。但宜家佢夠錢**餵**飽啲細路，最細嗰個仲要得兩歲。**Afia**，星期五出世；**Abimbola**，含住金鎖匙出世但一直做窮人；**Amara**，曾經優雅但宜家嚴重缺乏蛋白質而肚大頭禿；**Chi**、**Ke**、**Re**、**Po**，頭髮枯旱眼裏有沙**嘅**四胞胎。

He made things happen because, after the wife . . . Fourteen options still.

佢做咗，因為老婆之後……仲有十四個選擇。

Afia, fifth of fourteen motherless ones

Afia，十四個喪母子女中排行第五嗰個

I am a broken egg on a blistered road. A dying bird on a razor-wire fence. The jackal trots this way, that way, sizing up how to eat me. My nostalgia is here again, no school, no soup. Just an empty sky whistling as we bury our dead. I am a marked card—red marks the spot. The arrow will whiz into the eye of a dried-up fountain. Are you my mother? There's a skeleton trapped in the black mamba's hissing. Grey feathers swirling the wrong way.

我係爛溶溶路上**嘅**碎蛋；我係刀片鐵絲網上垂死**嘅**雀仔。隻豺狼**踱嚟踱**去，度緊點樣食咗我。我又開始念舊喇，無學校、無湯，只有空洞嘅天喺我哋自我埋葬時呼嘯；我係被標記嘅卡——一點紅。支箭會呼一聲直插乾涸嘅泉眼。你係咪我媽咪？有副骷髏骨被黑曼巴蛇嘅嘶嘶聲困住。灰羽毛以錯嘅方式旋轉。

The youngest child speaks

最細嗰個話

I'm in search of something I don't know. There's a hand and a gaze, a smile and a scent. It's a comfort, it's a warmth. I don't remember the face that comes and goes, the love that is a crack. It's complicated, it's unsafe. Blurred and full of crumble.

我搵緊一啲我都唔知係乜嘢嘢。有手同目光、笑容同香味。係一種舒適，一份溫暖；我唔記得嚟完又去嘅樣、有裂痕嘅愛。係複雜，亦唔安全，模糊而佈滿碎屑。

Nostalgia, a great-uncle with empty sacks, an odour of mothballs in his breath, his eyes a fortress against hope. You think of this moment, over and over, wishing you and the rest of the world remembered different.

念舊，一個拎住空袋嘅叔公，臭丸味嘅口氣，佢嘅眼睛係針對希望嘅要塞。你諗起呢刻，一次又一次，但願**你**同所有人都可以記得唔一樣**嘅**世界。

Black Queen

Nuzo Onoh

ΩΩΩ

GRANDFATHER told us that the River Omambalu was a woman, unfathomable and unpredictable like most women are. And, just like every scorned woman, her grudge was deep and her spite, deadly. He had a name for the river; he called her Black Queen. Grandfather said that despite all our sacrifices to her, it was impossible to tell when her mood would change and her tumultuous rage, turn on all of us. Grandfather said we must therefore, always treat Black Queen with respect, with greater respect than we accorded him, which was a riverful of respect, seeing as he was the most respected of elders in our small riverine village, nestled behind the thick forest of towering trees that formed a living barrier, one-mile-long, between us and Black Queen. There were Iroko, Cedar, Gum, and Melina trees thriving inside the great rainforest that housed the mischievous Monkeys and moody Chimpanzees, the graceful Antelopes and crying Bushbabies, as well as birds, fowls, insects, and reptiles in every size, shape, and colour.

'What will happen if we don't respect Black Queen?' Ifedi, my little sister asked, her wide eyes bright with the seeking light that had earned her the nickname of *"Onye-ajuju"*, meaning, "The Questioner".

'Then she'll open her mighty jaws like a great monster and swallow us up inside her black bowels,' Grandfather said.

'Even you, too?' Ifedi asked, her eyes wide with disbelief.

'Even me too,' Grandfather confirmed, nodding his grey head.

We all looked at ourselves with wonder, my siblings, half-siblings, cousins, and the rest of the clans-children gathered under the great Mango tree in our large hamlet to listen to my Grandfather's nightly tales of mystery and lore. It was impossible to us that anything, even Black Queen herself, could defeat our great hero. You see, Grandfather was the strongest and wisest man in our village. He was the only person to have survived the African Rock Python's squeeze and even more incredibly, succeeded in destroying that ancient reptile in their deadly combat inside the great forest. Prior to Grandfather's feat, uncountable villagers had forfeited their souls to the mortal squeeze of that fearsome reptile, who struck with uncanny intelligence and cunning malignancy, creating widows and widowers, orphans and ruined clans in both our village and the other small villages that bordered the thick forest which led to the Omambalu river. Grandfather's right arm had been his salvation, together with the African porcupine trapped inside his hunting bag. He had been able to stick out his right arm, and with *Amadioha*-might, shoved the spiky rodent into the Python's jaw as it leaned in for the kill. The spikes pierced the reptile's throat, forcing it to untangle its lethal coil on Grandfather's body in a frenzy of pain and confusion. Grandfather had been able to stab it multiple times with his hunting spear till he finally defeated that forest terror.

Every child, woman, and adult in the village and beyond, knew the story of Grandfather's duel with the great reptile monster. It had long gone down in the annals of our village lore, and we his family and kinsmen, basked in the pride of his glory. As a reward, the village elders gave Grandfather the head of the Python to feast upon, while the menfolk shared the rest of the meat, roasted in the open fires underneath the full moon, amidst dancing, drumming, and celebratory songs. It was said that when Grandfather ate the great reptile's head, he ingested its ancient wisdom, knowledge so powerful that it knocked him out for several days, until everyone feared he might never recover.

But recover he did, on the fifth day, when the moon was so swollen it hung low on the skies like an overripe fruit ready to burst. The first word Grandfather spoke on opening his eyes, was that the villagers should start harvesting their farmlands without delay; because in three days, he said, the heavens would darken at noonday and the sun shall be hidden from our eyes, bringing misery to our hamlets. Grandfather's eyes had been chalk-white as he spoke, the dark pupils swallowed behind his sockets. No one doubted his words, as they knew he now spoke with the voice of the oracle as a result of the wisdom received from the great reptile's head.

People started harvesting their corn cobs, *Akidi* beans, spinach and *Ugu* leaves, peppers, and even their cassava and yam tubers, the two king-crops that generally took longer to harvest. It wasn't much to boast about, since we were a riverine community and depended more on our fishing than our farming. Still, every morsel yielded from the soil was something to value and the villagers worked like soldier-ants to harvest every single seed from our farms. And on the third day, just as Grandfather prophesied, the skies went black in the middle of the day as the ferocious swarm of locusts descended on our village in their fearsome multitudes, devouring everything in their path.

The locusts remained for just a day and a night, but by the time they finally departed after the villagers had chased them away with a cacophony of noises, shrieks, drums, clashing metal pots, clapping and war songs, they had reduced our farmlands to brown barrenness. Everybody knew that, but for Grandfather's prediction, we would have lost our entire crop to the pestilence and faced famine and starvation. And our hamlet soon filled with the offerings from our grateful villagers, ranging from chickens to Palmwine kegs, goats and even a couple of *Akwete* calico wrappers.

From that terrible day of the locusts, Grandfather became the village's wise Seer, and everyone came to him for advice, and to settle family quarrels and neighbourly disputes. Once in a while, after that first spectacular prophecy, he would receive visions from the oracles, but not frequently. But when he spoke, people listened, and when he told us to treat Black Queen with respect, with greater respect than we accorded him, everybody heard his words, and everybody obeyed.

ΩΩΩ

Crawling her winding flow along the contours of our village, Black Queen was as beautiful as she was terrifying. Her water-skin was as black as ebony and glistened as if greased with palm-kennel oil. She was so black that on still moonless nights, when the sky god enjoyed the secret pleasures of his rotund silver-wife, one could easily mistake her for the wide asphalt road that led to Onitsha town, save for the soft sighs she made as she glided her wet and meandering course along the sandy shoreline. Most days, her flow was steady, smooth and serene in her spectacular, shimmering blackness, and my skin never ceased to break out in goosebumps whenever I viewed her undulating waves each morning I visited with my family for our ablutions. Even the numerous fishing boats dotted along her black expanse, could never dent her menacing dark allure. I remember I used to be so terrified of Black Queen that I would refuse to bathe in the river like the rest of the villagers. Even when my mother invited me to try the smaller backwater enclave Black Queen had carved for our people before the birth of our ancestors, the encircled pond where the older women bathed in some privacy, I still recoiled from her cold and unfathomable embrace. Her black, shimmering surface filled me with so much terror that I would keep my eyes shut as I filled my clay-pot with enough water to wash my body in the safe privacy of our hamlet. The only time I felt safe was when I accompanied Grandfather to her shores to offer sacrifices to her. The bowl of cooked food always felt warm and comforting in my hands, and the tantalising aroma never failed to make me wish I were as important as Black Queen, so that I could get offered such delicious sacrifices.

Grandfather said Black Queen used to be married to the sky god, *Amadioha*, he of the thunderous voice and fiery lightning eyes. Theirs was a union of harmony and peace until the sky god betrayed her love and married two fat brides on the same day, the Night-Queen, *Ọwa,* with her cold, silvery sheen, and the Day-Queen, *Awu*, with her blazing golden rays. In fury, Black Queen appealed to the Earth-Mother, *Anά,* for refuge. *Anά* welcomed her like a daughter and gave her the piece of earth in our village, where she curved her long twisty route into the hard soil.

In revenge, the sky god pelted both the Earth-Mother and Black Queen with his hard rain-spit and lightning strikes from his blazing eyes. And on dark windy nights, when *Amadioha*'s thunderstorm caused Black Queen to rage and foam, her wave-fists raised in fury at her philandering sky lord, the villagers quaked inside their dark huts as her waves crashed in deadly combat against herself and the unfortunate villagers who lived nearest to the shorelines. Thankfully, Black Queen's fury was always short-lived and her benevolence, steadfast.

Grandfather told us all these wonderful tales during the numerous story sessions held underneath the silvery glow of the pregnant Night-Queen, just before she gave birth to her litter of glittering stars. The blaze from the open fires would warm our faces as we listened with hushed breaths to Grandfather's raspy sing-song voice, the aroma of roasting sweetcorn cobs from our farmland tantalising our tastebuds. He said that in the old days, our people used to sacrifice the most beautiful virgins to appease Black Queen, since it was known that she loathed beautiful women. She viewed them as rivals, eternally fearful her fickle husband might snatch them from earth as wives, giving birth to new moons or suns in the endless skies. Grandfather said that as long as Black Queen received her virgin sacrifices, her rage never harmed the villagers and she rewarded us with more fish than we could consume, enough fish for us to sell to the other land-locked villages who craved the wonderful gift given us by our river deity.

However, with the arrival of the gun-wielding police force in our local government, our villagers ceased the practice of human sacrifices to Black Queen, substituting virgins with cows, sheep and chickens, although it was whispered that on some secret occasions, a lost stranger, some female albino, a dwarf female, or an accursed witch from the neighbouring villages, were sacrificed in the deep of night to appease Black Queen. This was to mitigate the terrible effects of her anger over the cessation of human sacrifices, as she had taken to sporadically drowning young women from our village who were foolish enough to venture far from the beach for their ablutions.

Grandfather told us that during the rainy season, Black Queen raged and wept for her lost love, her spuming waves crashing against the beach and flooding the red mud-huts dotting the shoreline. The villagers have long learnt to evacuate their huts in those dire months to give her the privacy to mourn. Fishing was generally abandoned for farming and hunting during those few months of supernatural grief, thereby enabling our people to feed off both the land and the river. Listening to Grandfather's tales, my heart would quiver with a masochistic combination of thrill and terror. I wanted to hear more about our fearsome and powerful river deity, yet the more I heard, the more I quaked. I was ashamed of my cowardice and irrational fear, coupled with the relentless teasing and bullying by my siblings and village children. But my terror of Black Queen was greater than my shame, and it stayed with me through those unforgettable days of my childhood, till I sprouted into the young marriage-age woman that I am today.

ΩΩΩ

Grandfather is now dead, and his wonderful stories have died with him, together with the wisdom that had guided our village through the long years of lively serenity. I doubt if anyone remembers his warnings to treat Black Queen with respect, certainly not the greedy villagers who now follow the lead of the fat one they call Eze, the stupid village boy who somehow managed to mould himself into a man of importance in the big city of Lagos, another riverine place like our village, but from what I've heard, much larger and more important than our tiny, remote village. I knew Eze when he was a bare-feet, bare-chested runt, with snot dripping down his dirty face and mosquito bites crusting his skin with sores. But now, he's worshipped by the villagers like a deity, just because he freed them from their servitude to Black Queen and brought them easy wealth and the freedom to drown themselves in the fiery drinks supplied by Eze's friends, the Chinese bosses.

It all started on the day Eze drove into the village with a group of men, men with black skin like us, but dressed in the white people's black suits, white shirts, and knotted ties. They were accompanied by two camouflage-coloured jeeps crammed with men in military uniforms and evil-looking long guns slung low across their shoulders. All the strangers wore dark sunglasses and it was impossible to read the truth in their eyes as they spoke to our elders. Eze, the snot-nosed kid of our childhood days, was their spokesperson.

I remember that fateful day as if it were carved into my skin with lightning strikes. It was on a Friday afternoon and the midday sun rode high in the sky, while the air was somnambulant with the aroma of cooking foods, Hammattan dust, and that peculiar musky smell of Black Queen, which could only be experienced, but could never be truly described. The happy thrills of the village children fought for dominance over the bleating of the goats and the lazy, gossipy chirps of the womenfolk, while occasionally, the mechanical sound of a passing bus at the sole village asphalt road, reminded us that we were part of the twenty-first century.

I recall that I had just finished hanging the laundry on the high cassava stalks that formed the ringed fencing of our hamlet, when I heard the incredible sounds of several motor-vehicles rumbling down the dust-path that led to our compound. In the days when Grandfather lived and prophesied, that path had been constructed by the one-score age group, to accommodate the myriad of visitors that trooped to our compound to seek his wisdom. But since he slept with the ancestors, the path had ceased to see much traffic, save for the villagers, some stray *Ekuke* mongrel dogs, and the occasional bicycles and three-wheeled barrows.

So, the sight of the convoy of motor-vehicles driving into the dust-path on that bright Friday afternoon quickly sent the entire village population outside our hamlet. They congregated in their hordes, children, women and adults, curiosity layering their sweaty faces. I joined my father, his four wives and my twenty-three siblings, both womb-siblings and half-siblings, as we all joined the rest of the villagers surrounding the unexpected and unannounced strangers in our midst.

Eze spoke at length, cracking jokes and laughing loudly at his own jokes. When he had finally tired of hearing his own voice and sweating under his heavy *Agbada* flowing gown, he invited the elders to inspect the metal boxes the strangers had brought along with them. The men with the long guns quickly surrounded the boxes, their guns cocked, and pointing threateningly up at the sky. But one of the strangers, most likely their leader, and the fattest and loudest of the visitors, dismissed the uniformed men with an imperious wave of his ringed hands. He was dressed in a black three-piece suit and darker sunglasses, and sweated profusely under the scorching heat, his white handkerchief glued to his broad face. The two massive wristwatches adorning each fleshy wrist, winked brightly in the midday blaze as he urged our elders to draw closer to the open boxes.

I heard the elders gasped audibly when they saw what was contained inside the metal boxes. Soon everybody surged forward to get a view of the mysterious boxes. I also looked, and what I saw caused my eyes to goggle. There were six great metal boxes filled with countless bundles of *Naira* notes, in fact, more money than our entire village had ever possessed in our lifetime. As people gasped in awe, the obese leader began to speak in a voice that was as stentorian as his superior face. He explained to the villagers that the money was the first instalment for the commercial deforestation and sand-mining agreement our government had signed with the Chinese foreign investors.

People looked at him with perplexed frowns, shoulders shrugging indifferently, as his words made no sense to any of us. Moreover, he spoke in formal English grammar, instead of the pigeon-English which most of the villagers understood. Seeing our baffled expressions, Eze quickly took over from the stranger. Speaking in our local dialect, Eze explained that the deal, which involved the large-scale felling of the trees in our lush forest, as well as the industrial collection of the fine, white sand along our beaches, would be beneficial to our community in the immediate and long term. He said the deal would ensure we would no longer need to rely solely on fishing for our livelihood, and could start replacing our red-mud huts with cement houses, complete with shiny corrugated sheets for our roofs, instead of the old thatched eyesores in the village. Eze even threw in the possibility of electricity, stating that the Chinese miners would be building their own secluded village near our village, as well as a larger, enclosed quarters for their local workers. Our young men, of course, would be given priority in the recruitment drive, thereby, bringing further wealth into our village. The money boxes, lease money for our lands, forest and beaches, would continue to arrive every month as long as the village community did not cause any unrest or disrupt the project.

Eze's words were like nectar to the entire village and in no time, large jars of palm-wine were brought out to celebrate the deal. My father and our entire clan were amongst the people celebrating the lucrative deal with Eze's companions, with a big ram butchered roasted under the open flames in our hamlet to mark the great event. I also joined the dancing women in the merriment, lured by the prospect of electricity and the brightness I had seen a few times when I visited the large city east of our village, with its big houses, wide roads, colourful shops, and electric-bright nights. I still nursed the old contempt I always had for Eze from our childhood days when he used to spy at me washing my body behind my mother's hut. But, if he was going to bring us the miracle of electricity, then I was ready to forget his pervy lechery and let bygones be bygones.

ΩΩΩ

A year after the elders accepted Eze's money boxes, another group of visitors arrived unexpectedly at our village, this time in a delegation that comprised of both men and women, including a young white man with hair the colour of the Day-Queen, *Awu.* Just like Eze's delegation, the new group of strangers arrived in motor-vehicles, albeit without the armed, uniformed men. Once again, they parked their two vehicles outside our hamlet and within minutes, a crowd of villagers surrounded them, mainly women, children and the elders, since most of the adults were absent, busy working at the Chinese mining sites.

The new visitors were led by a young man who introduced himself as Chudi. I did not think his age surpassed my twenty years by more than eight years, yet, when he spoke, he spoke with the authority of an elder. He spoke the white man's language from the nose, just like the yellow-haired white man in their group, yet, he also spoke pigeon English like a native. Chudi was tall and lean, his close-cropped hair a deep black colour, just like his eyes, which fixed me with intensity as he addressed our community underneath the roasting heat of the Day-Queen's rays.

Chudi and his group begged us to reject the deal Eze had brought to our village. They said the deforestation and sand-mining were dangerous to our village and the earth's climate and would bring floods and devastation to us. They said the normal functioning of the ecosystem was being ruthlessly destroyed by the unethical activities of the Chinese miners, in cahoots with our corrupt government. Chudi and his companions used miniature toy trees and several props, including plastic animals, to explain the dangers posed to our environment by the large-scale felling of trees and sand-mining, which was going on even as they spoke. The deafening sounds of heavy lorries and sawing machinery in the background failed to drown out their desperate pleas.

I remember that Chudi spoke with passion and urgency, his deep voice coaxing as he urged us to fight for our heritage and preserve our children's future. His eyes seemed to return to my face several times as he spoke, as if he felt that mine was the one face in the crowd of uneducated villagers that was connecting with his words. To my shame, I confess that it wasn't so much his words I connected with, but rather, his voice; the deep, resonate tone that sent delicious shivers coursing through my body, making me wish I could hear the special music of his voice for the rest of my life. I kept staring at him like a python-hypnotised fool, smiling when he smiled, frowning when he frowned, and nodding when he nodded.

A handful of the village youths who were off work for the day, shouted Chudi down, while the women sang mocking songs, shaking their stupendous bottoms rudely at him. The children, encouraged by the adults, snatched their props and threw fistfuls of sand at them. Everyone could see they had no gun-toting soldiers to protect them, so there was no need to fear them, not even with the red-skinned white man in their entourage, who looked about to faint in the boiling midday heat. Nobody wanted to hear Chudi's words. The villagers called him a snake, with a forked tongue that spoke falsehood—*Black Queen is as she has always been; our village has changed for the better as any fool can see. Why, even the route to the river is now clear, easy and safe for the villagers to use, all thanks to the felling of the trees by the Chinese bosses. Nobody fears the aggressive Chimpanzees and deadly Cobras, which have mostly vanished from the forest with the deforestation project. Clearly, Chudi and his group belong to a different, envious community, who resent our good fortune and unexpected wealth. Our children's futures are very secure, thank you very much, and good riddance to your crazy garbage.* The villagers screeched their angry thoughts in loud voices.

They were right. Our village was indeed thriving, with new cement houses springing up every week in the lush landscape. Even my father had demolished several of the huts in our hamlet, to build an impressive cement-block bungalow for himself and his four wives. The rest of the children still continued to occupy the old huts. We now had a couple of drinking bars in the village, where the menfolk went to drink and enjoy the sudden wealth that flowed from the forests and beaches into our village coffers. Papa Li Wei's new grocery shop now offered us amazing foodstuff like nothing we'd ever seen, save on the big outdoor cinema the Chinese bosses screened for us once every month. Canned drinks, packet noodles, soft white loaves of the sweetest bread, even cakes and biscuits, were now everyday treats for us. Yes; Eze had told us half-truths, but it didn't seem to bother anyone. The Chinese bosses didn't bring our village electricity as he'd promised. Instead, the bright lights blazed only at the two local bars, the chief's house, Papa Li Wei's grocery store, and of course, Eze's house. The rest of us remained in darkness, except on those nights when the Night-Queen, *Ọwa*, hung pregnant and heavy in the skies, and blessed our lands with her bright glow.

I saw the defeated and hopeless look in Chudi's eyes as they turned to depart from our village after their abortive mission. It touched something in my soul. Suddenly, in his words, I heard the wisdom of my late grandfather, and in that minute, my heart feared the vengeance of Black Queen as never before. I didn't need anyone to tell me what I could already see, what I knew like a mother knows her child; that the villagers had ceased to treat Black Queen with respect, the great respect Grandfather had demanded in the days he walked the earth. The elders no longer sacrificed animals to her since the arrival of the Chinese bosses and their metal boxes of *Naira* banknotes. The workmen dumped all their building waste inside her black bowels, while the debris from the murdered trees ruined her once dark beauty, giving her a dull, murky sheen. When I went to collect water for my bath, I found her surface layered with assorted cans, bottles, plastics, bread wrappings, discarded clothing and cardboard papers.

One day, I caught one of my younger half-siblings chucking his empty Cola can into the river as I filled my bucket with water. I cuffed his ears and warned him to be more respectful of Black Queen. The lout ran home and reported me to his mother, who slapped me, resulting in a big fight between her and my mother. Papa was angry with me when he found out what I had done.

'Are you the river's keeper, you foolish girl?' he shouted at me, his eyes red with rage. 'Did Omambalu tell you it's unhappy because of the stuff thrown into it, eh? What do you think rivers are meant for, if not to carry away rubbish? Do you want to go and tell our Chinese bosses not to throw things into the river, and to take their money and go away so our village can starve and suffer as in the past?' Papa hissed loudly. 'Let this be the last time I hear that you've hit any of your siblings because of the river, do you hear me?'

I heard him. Everybody heard our father, and from that day, my half-siblings and the rest of the clans-children took joy in provoking me by throwing every kind of rubbish into Black Queen whenever I was around, calling out teasing insults and laughing at my scowls. One of the idiots even made it a point of duty to piss into the river whenever I arrived with my bucket, waiting for me to hit him as I itched to do, so he could get me into trouble with our father. I couldn't believe how quickly everyone had forgot Grandfather's teachings, and my sense of betrayal on his behalf was great.

Still, I couldn't blame them entirely in all fairness; after all, they saw the adults disrespecting Black Queen on a daily basis, and figured she was now fair game for all. Even the shoreline villagers no longer accorded her the privacy to mourn her lost love as they used to do in the past. Their houses were now built with strong cement blocks, instead of the red mud and straw roofing of old, and they could now climb to the decked roofs of their homes to take refuge when Black Queen flooded their houses in her grief.

Black Queen was now a dead queen, her once smooth skin decayed into putrid rottenness by the polluted poisons that consumed her former glory. She chugged along pathetically, slow and clumsy, humiliated and hopeless, just like a once beautiful woman limping on amputated limbs. If Grandfather lived, he would weep for her ruined beauty, the death of her glossy blackness and the shameful proof of her disrespect littering her filthy surface. So, as Chudi and his group spoke to us on that unforgettable afternoon, I recognised the wisdom in their words and prayed with everything in me that the others heard as well. As I watched them drive away in their dusty Land Rover Discovery, I knew with a feeling of embarrassed excitement, that my heart also yearned to hear the secrets of Chudi's heart.

ΩΩΩ

Chudi made several trips to our village after that first futile visit, sometimes with his friends, and at other times, by himself. When he came alone, I knew he came mainly to see me, even as he tried to sway the villagers to his mission. Despite the difference in our social and academic status, our hearts quickly recognised themselves as equals. He didn't mind that my education ended after my third year in the village secondary school, while he had two university degrees to his name. He called me his beautiful treasure and said that my eyes were precious opals, my braided hair, strings of black pearls, and my soul, a priceless diamond, pure, clear, and bright. His words were like music I'd never heard, wondrous poetry unlike anything ever spoken by man or the gods. And as our relationship blossomed, I started to believe that I was indeed a beautiful and precious stone, nestled snugly in the hands of a master jeweller. Chudi started to bring me books to read, what he called African classics – Chinua Achebe, Wole Soyinka, Ben Okri, Credo Mutwa, and many other amazing works by geniuses blessed specially by the gods of words and the ancestors of imagination.

When Chudi asked my father for my hand in marriage several months later, I knew that all my yearnings had been granted by my ancestors. The womenfolk cautioned me about marrying "The crazy one" as they affectionately, yet, contemptuously called Chudi. They warned me I was making a great mistake by leaving the safety of our village for the big city, with a book-crazy man whose mind bordered on lunacy. I know my mother would have urged me to reconsider if my spinster status hadn't become a bother to her. My siblings said they always knew I would end up marrying someone as crazy as I was, recalling my irrational fear of Black Queen and my refusal to bathe in her cool waters as everyone else in the village did. Even the fat lout, Eze, decided to save me from my insanity, doing me the favour of offering to make me his second wife. He flashed his two Chinese companions as enticement and proof of his elevated status, his beer-bloated flesh reeking of perfume overdose and stale sweat.

I did little to hide the scorn in my eyes and my voice as I coldly declined his proposal and bowed my way out of his companions' presence. I liked the Chinese bosses even though I hated what they were doing to our village, and especially to Black Queen. They were always polite and smiling, bowing to us and offering our children treats and gifts. In fact, some of them already spoke our tongue with impressive dexterity, and even ate our chilli-heavy dishes without blinking. The village rumour mill even had it that one of the bosses was planning on making the skinny hog, Adaku, his bride, the poor man. We heard that the Chinese liked their women small and skinny like Adaku, but we all feared that this time, they had struck a bad bargain. Everyone said Adaku would soon eat her betrothed out of hut and hamlet in no time and still remain as bony as a stick.

When Adaku was a child, the villagers used to curse her parents for being stingy with her meals, especially since she was their only child. It wasn't until the witchdoctor confirmed that she was an *Ayọmuwa*, "a returned", one of the reincarnated souls with unfinished business, that people began to pity her afflicted parents. The witchdoctor said Adaku was the reincarnate of Ugodi the widow, who had died of starvation and swore that in her next incarnation, she would eat till there was nothing left in the world to eat. Ugodi the widow also swore to remain skinny no matter how much she was fed, so as to torture and shame her family and remind them of how badly she'd been treated in her former life. But worst of all, she had returned with a vengeful curse, ensuring her new parents would have no other living child apart from her, to ensure no other mouths competed for her food. Adaku's mother and stepmother had both experienced so many spontaneous miscarriages since her birth, that her father had finally resigned himself to the sad reality of witnessing the end of his bloodline, since such returned souls were generally known to die at a young age. My mother said she thought Adaku was marrying the Chinese boss because he was the only man rich enough to afford her hunger.

Yes, I liked the Chinese bosses a lot, and under normal circumstances, wouldn't have minded living side by side with them in our village. But

Chudi and his friends from the environmental NGO had filled my head with such terrifying knowledge that I now knew the Chinese activities in our forests and beaches were a slow poison, a simmering plague waiting to devastate not just our village, but the broader universe in the long run. I wondered if I was the only one to notice Black Queen raged more frequently than before, grieving for her lost love both during the rainy season, the dry season, and even the dusty Harmattan season. She had never behaved with such randomness and fury in Grandfather's days, yet, it was as if our people's memories had died on the day Eze brought his metal boxes of blood money into our village square.

ΩΩΩ

Grandfather visited me for the first time in the week I was about to have my traditional marriage to Chudi. It happened strangely on a clear bright morning when our hamlet teamed with clans-women gossiping about my upcoming marriage, while the children played as was their habit in the sandy and dusty terrain, chasing lizards and grass-hoppers while fighting, crying, singing, laughing, or shouting for the sheer stupidity of it. I was feeling inexplicably sad, dreading the prospect of leaving the familiarity of my people and my village for the big city of Onitsha where Chudi lived. Of course, I loved my fiancé and was looking forward to being with him for the rest of my life, but still, a part of me feared the unknown and the total permanency of my separation from my family.

Needing solitude to work through my emotions and thoughts, I wandered into Grandfather's old hut, located right in the centre of the hamlet, where his grave mound was raised, to watch over his family and keep us from harm. Everybody went to visit Grandfather's Grave-hut whenever they had a burden or question in their hearts, and I was lucky and thankful that the hut was empty of supplicants that morning as I wandered into its gloomy cocoon.

With deep reverence, I bowed low before the elevated mud-grave, placed the bottle of Coca-Cola I had bought for him from Papa Li Wei's shop, before sitting on the hard floor by his grave-mound. I folded my legs under me and clasped my hands together, as I lowered my head in respect. Grandfather had slept before the arrival of the bosses and their wonderous foods, and I always made it a point of duty to bring him different treats from the white man's world to sample whenever I visited.

The Grave-hut was peaceful, silent, and blissfully cool as ever. It was the only place in the hamlet and possibly, the entire village, guaranteed to be almost chilly regardless of the scorching sun, and I sometimes went in there just to get away from the heat instead of communing with Grandfather. But, today, my comfort was the last thing on my mind. I just wanted to share my worries with him and seek his advice. I knew that he would visit me later in my dreams to give me the answers I sought, just as he was known to do since he slept. Numerous villagers claimed to have had visitations in their dreams, and I knew they spoke with truth, because I too had experienced the same dream-visits from Grandfather, just like my family and clans-people.

In no time, I was baring my soul to Grandfather, tears trickling down my cheeks as I spoke in hushed tones, fearful of disturbing his sleep, just in case he was yet to rise up in the realm of the ancestors, seeing as it was still somewhat early in the morning. I must have spoken for several minutes before I became suddenly conscious of an unsettling quality in the air. The chilly air became colder, like the iced drinks from Papa Li Wei's freezer. I shivered, wrapping my arms around myself. Just then, the bottle of Coca-Cola I'd placed on Grandfather's grave mound trembled, tottered, and before my incredulous eyes, fell to the floor, shattering the bottle in a million sharp fragments and wasting the precious dark drink on the now-damp soil.

As I scrambled to my feet, Grandfather materialised right before my stunned gaze, right in front of the wooden door, blocking my escape route. For, my first instinct after my initial scream was to run, a desperate flight bred from the terror thuds in my heart and the terrified swelling of my head. I was shaking, my mouth quivering with whispered gasps that could only repeat one word with idiotic repetitiveness...*Ghost! Ghost! Ghost!* That was until I saw something that stunned me and killed my terror. I saw a great river of tears crawling down Grandfather's cheeks like the former gentle flow of Black Queen's waters. In all my life, I had never seen my grandfather cry, not even as he lay dying from the painful venom of the snake-bite that stole his life, a snake believed to be the child of the great python Grandfather had killed in the forest, now come to avenge its murdered parent. But now, my dead grandfather stood before me, crying silently, the tears flowing in an endless river with countless tributaries.

'Grandfather…Big Papa…why do you cry?' I managed to whisper, my eyes wide with confusion, and my heart twisted with soul-crushing pity. Grandfather's ghost, so solid and real, just like a living human, merely shook his head, his movement laborious, and pathetic. Then in a blink, just as its appearance had occurred, he vanished, right before my incredulous eyes. With his vanishing, my terror returned, and I fled the Grave-hut on feet as fast and light as the antelope's, my heart pounding louder than the masquerade drums. In my blind terror, I almost crashed into my little sister, Ifedi, the one affectionately nicknamed *"Onye-ajuju"*, meaning, "The Questioner", she of the countless questions in our childhood days, and even into our adulthood.

Grandfather used to say that there were two kinds of questioners in the world. First, were the questioners that asked questions to elevate their minds, seek enlightenment and truth. The other were the questioners that asked questions just for the sheer bloody-mindedness of it, simply to be awkward and troublesome. My sister, Ifedi, sadly fell into the second category. Though Grandfather had answered her uncountable questions about

Black Queen in our childhood days, she and her band of hoydens persisted in littering the river with their empty drink-cans, biscuit wrappers and even their soiled period pads, a new-found luxury purchased from Papa Li Wei's shop. Still, despite her recalcitrance, I loved Ifedi the best of all my siblings because she was without malice, just exceedingly playful and mischievous.

Without catching my breath, I soon began to spill my terrifying experience inside Grandfather's Grave-gut, my body pouring with sweat of terror, made worse by the blistering heat. Ifedi listened with wide-eyed awe to my story before reverting to her default modus operandi.

'Are you sure you didn't fall asleep while meditating and dreamt it all?' she asked, peering intently into my eyes as if seeking lunacy or idiocy.

'No, I didn't. I tell you, I saw Grandfather as clearly as I'm seeing you now,'

'And you insist he said nothing, absolutely nothing, eh? So, why do you think he appeared to you then?'

'If I knew, do you think I'd be asking you about it?'

'Do you think we should tell Papa about it?'

'No,' I shuddered. The last person I wanted to hear about it was our father. I knew he would cuff my ears for spreading lies and frightening the children in the hamlet with my tale of hauntings. Everyone would be terrified to visit the Grave-hut if they believed it was now haunted, even as we all loved and revered Grandfather. Dream haunting was the acceptable type of haunting in our community, not the real, visible ghost haunting. 'No, don't tell anyone about this, Ifedi; you swear?'

Ifedi nodded. 'I swear on Grandfather's grave. But, do you think he'll visit you again?'

I shrugged. 'I don't know. He didn't say anything, but there must be something worrying him at the ancestors' realm and causing him not to rest, as well as the tears. I'm thinking I should go back to the Grave-hut and see if he'll appear again and maybe say something this time,'

'Aren't you afraid?' Ifedi's eyes were wide with anticipated fear, as if she were already seeing Grandfather's ghost.

'I am, but I'm not, if you get my meaning,' I looked into a space beyond her curious face, seeing Grandfather's beloved face and the ubiquitous bowl of peanuts all ready for our *Tales-by-Moonlight* underneath the Mango tree in my happy childhood years. In the gentle midday breeze, I heard his raspy voice weaving magic and bliss into our souls, and suddenly, an overwhelming sense of loss washed over me. *If only Grandfather would come back again...if only I could see him just one more time as a living person and not as a ghost.*

'Do you want me to come with you to the Grave-hut?' Ifedi offered generously, though the terror in her eyes told me it was the very last thing she wanted to do.

'No, it's alright,' I smiled, seeing the relief in her eyes. 'I think he wants to talk to me alone. I'll return again tomorrow morning and see if he'll appear. But remember, not a word to anyone, okay?

'Okay,' Ifedi hugged me tightly before skipping off, no doubt, to re-join her group of rowdy teenage girls. I stood at the same spot for several minutes, lost in a world of memories and yearning, a lost world of innocence and happiness, a paradise that was created by Grandfather and was painfully lost when he slept. In that second, I knew that I would give anything and everything to see my grandfather one more time, even if it meant seeing him as a ghost.

The next morning, just as I expected, Grandfather's ghost appeared once again. And just like the previous day, he shattered the bottle of Coca-Cola I offered him, wasting the drink just as before. I was starting to think that Grandfather didn't like this particular white man's drink, and made a mental note to bring him something different in future. This time, Grandfather cried black tears, tears so dark they resembled the black colour of Black Queen's waters in her former glorious days, before the Chinese bosses and our government and village accomplices, ruined her spectacular beauty.

'Grandfather…please tell me why you cry so sadly?' I pleaded, this time my voice stronger, louder. He opened his mouth to speak, but nothing came out of it, no sound, not even a whisper. And yet, the black tears wouldn't stop drowning his face in a black flood of grief. When he vanished, I again sought the company of my sister and narrated my latest haunting.

'Do you think you should maybe take him something sweet to cheer him up, so he can stop crying and talk?' Ifedi asked, reaching into her pocket and coming up with a bar of chocolate. 'Here, you can have my chocolate, and don't forget to tell Grandfather that I gave it to you, so we can share whatever blessings he gives you; you promise?'

'I promise,' I hugged her, thinking my sister was very wise despite her air-headedness. The next morning, when Grandfather appeared to me for the third and final time, I wished I'd never returned to that Grave-hut that was now starting to be the saddest place on earth for me. This time, the chocolate bar didn't just shake on his grave, it flew right off the mound in a violent hurl, smashing into the mud-wall just as Grandfather materialised, howling terror into my heart. His face dripped blood, a riverful of blood-tears that coated his body with fire. He glowed as he'd never glowed in the past, finally looking like the true ghost that he was. And from his wide mouth issued forth the most bone-chilling howl ever heard by human ears, shrieks that curdled my blood and froze my limbs. I didn't need to ask him any questions as in the past, because this time, he answered my unspoken thoughts.

'Leave.... everybody leave now...danger...Black Queen...leave...leave...lea...'

By the time he vanished, I too was howling, my body drenched in terror-sweat as I stumbled out of the Grave-hut and rushed into Papa's new bungalow, hyperventilating between my tears and snivels. In no time, I was telling Papa and all gathered, including my mother, stepmothers, visiting clanswomen and adults, as well as some curious children who had followed my howls into the bungalow, everything that had occurred inside Grandfather's Grave-hut.

Papa listened to my incoherent babbling, his face growing more thunderous as I spoke, while the other adults all made horror-signs, casting the evil over their shoulders with their clicking fingers and hissing lips. When I was done, I wished I'd never spoken. Despite the fact I was engaged to be married in just a couple of days, Papa thrashed me till the women had to restrain him and remind him my body mustn't be too blemished for my upcoming marriage rite. He screamed and cursed me instead till my ears rung into near-deafness.

'Didn't I warn you about that blasted river, you stupid, crazy girl, eh?' Papa's shouted with rage-reddened eyes. 'Now, you decide to use your Grandfather's sacred name to impose your lunatic fiancé's will on us. It's a good thing you're getting married next tomorrow and leaving our village, hopefully for good. Leave my sight and don't let me see you again till the day your husband takes you and your crazy lies away from my hamlet. Go!'

I left, nursing my bruises and my pain. *What did I expect after all, that anyone would believe me, that anyone would pay heed to Grandfather's dire warning?* Grandfather had said that Black Queen's grudge was deep and her spite, deadly; just like the fury of every scorned woman. Now, with every hour that passed as I prepared for my marriage day, I sensed her grudge growing, her sighs louder, and her reek stronger, almost overpowering. And something deep within my soul dreaded the day her spite would finally spill. Like the doomed people in one of the books Chudi gave me to read, the foolish ones who loved and feasted with careless abandon beneath the boiling rage of their mountain-deity in a doomed city called Pompeii, our villagers sang, drank, and danced their days and nights away alongside the simmering rage of their abandoned and betrayed deity. A cold voice in my head told me that our day of reckoning was not far, that Black Queen would make us pay for our fickleness and gross disrespect.

ΩΩΩ

It happened exactly ten moons later, on the day I gave birth to our first son, Ikemefuna, meaning, "May my strength never be lost", named after my beloved grandfather. I heard the news first from my husband's lips, and then I saw it on the small television set in my hospital room. On the bright screen, I saw the terror that had blighted my child-hood and ruined my sleep, Black Queen's terrible, terrible rage, as her long-suppressed spite finally crashed into our village, her surging tidal waves wreaking appalling devastation on the land and its faithless people. The stunned newscaster, a young man around the same age as my husband, said that nobody, not a single soul in our village survived Black Queen's rage, not even the Chinese bosses and their local employees. He called it a tragedy of biblical proportions.

The news cameras beamed the apocalyptic images of our Armageddon from their hovering helicopters, sharing with the world the total annihilation of my history and my roots. Icy shivers broke my skin in goosebumps, hard tears quaking my body, pain and horror killing my soul. My family had been wiped off the face of the earth as if they never existed, my parents, stepmothers, siblings, half-siblings, cousins, aunts, uncles, in-laws and extended clansmen; my sweet sister, Ifedi, with her riverful of unfinished questions, swallowed in a blink, her questions never again to be heard or answered. And poor Adaku, whose great appetite will forever remain unsatisfied into her next reincarnation; all gone, all dead.

And my village, the place my ancestors and I had lived, laughed and cried, sang and danced for countless generations; it too had ceased to exist. In a blink of an eyelid, my past and the very source of my existence, Grandfather's Grave-hut, Papa's proud new cement bungalow, our bustling hamlet and neighbouring compounds, were all expunged from the annals of mankind, soon to be reduced to the realms of lore and folktales—*once upon a time, there lived a little village called Ukari, swallowed up by a long river called Black Queen...oh sweet Jesus, have pity!* There was now nobody to tell our story, nobody to remember us, our songs, our lore, our festivals and our culture. There was no one to dream for us and hope for our future. In a blink, it was over, wiped away as a teacher wipes the alphabets on the black board of life. I was the last of our community, the sole proof that our ancestors once existed.

And as I stared at the screen with shell-shocked horror, hot tears streaming down my cheeks, my stunned eyes staring disbelievingly at the still surging waves of our raging river deity cascading waves of vengeance on my vanquished village, a sad insignificance shrouded me in sudden, weary hopelessness. A great mind, a male genius, had once written that mankind was nothing but mites to the gods. The deities were immortal, he wrote, eternally trifling with us foolish humans for their merriment and spite. Black Queen had vented her deadly spleen on our feckless villagers, ignoring centuries of faithful service and loyalty by my people, forgetting the reverence of so many ancestors long gone, the same ancestors whose bloods flowed in the veins of those she had so coldly annihilated. And all for her foolish pride and our monumental stupidity, greed, and ignorance.

Chudi hugged me close, his arm wrapping my shoulders with love. The haunted look on his face fought with the anger raging in his eyes. Over and over, he cursed softly under his breath as he watched the horror unfolding on the television screen. I knew what he was thinking, what was causing his despair. *If only the villagers had heeded his warning, none of this would have happened.* Perhaps, he also thought that it was a good thing he'd married me and taken me away from the village before the disaster struck. Either way, nothing mattered anymore.

The tears continued to flow down my cheeks unchecked as I clutched my new son close to my chest, fearing Black Queen might yet snatch him away as well, should I relax my grip or my guard. I never trusted that deity and now, I have less reason to trust her. I guess the deities reflect the humans they spawned, selfish and fickle, spiteful and vengeful, but yet so beautiful, and so, so terribly flawed.

Behind 'So Close To Home'

Andrew Hook

When Eugen Bacon asked me if I'd like to participate in this project, I had literally just finished reading *Danged Black Thing*, her collection within which 'When the Water Stops' is published. I'd enjoyed the collection greatly, not simply because it includes 'Messier 94', which is a collaboration between the two of us, but because I enjoy what I've described as *her swift brushstrokes of characterisation that are met with poetic one-liners that set a scene or a mood.* 'When The Water Stops', a story—as if you don't know by now—of what might happen should a drought cause us to source other forms of liquid, including blood, was one of my favourites in the book. It infers a lot in a short space of time.

So when I received the email and the invite it was a no-brainer to say *yes*, but what should I write? I didn't want to embark on something set in the same location, or to tell the same story. I needed an angle.

When writing fiction, what has to come first for me is a title. Usually I start with one, and then an idea latches onto it, but this was almost the other way around. I thought of water motifs. In that connection, the Talking Heads song, 'Once in A Lifetime' popped into my head, with the lyrics *letting the days go by, let the water hold me down / letting the days go by, water flowing underground* demanding my attention, with 'Letting the Days Go By' being a possible title.

It certainly set the scene for the type of story I wanted to write, something wistful and melancholic, but not long after I discarded the idea. I was writing about 'When the Water Stops' after all, not riffing off 'Once in A Lifetime'. Sidling into my mind then came another title, 'So Much Water, So Close To Home', the short story by Raymond Carver. Whilst I've read and enjoyed the piece, I couldn't remember any details at all, but truncating that title to 'So Close To Home' seemed a perfect fit for what I wanted to write. In the West, we read a lot about natural disasters but—in the UK in any event—they rarely affect us. What if something were much closer to home than we usually experience? How does that affect us?

From the title, the story shift to the UK (for me, *close to home*) was obvious, and gave enough distance from the original idea to not simply replicate it. I thought of the disaster happening here. Of water being transported. Then made a note of what would become the first line: *They repurposed the filling stations.* I wondered what would happen if water were rationed, how might it be distributed. What might then happen should that distribution not be equal, would those trucks delivering water be attacked?

I'd recently watched a heartbreaking documentary about a number of Vietnamese who had suffocated to death whilst being transported illegally into the UK in the back of a truck. My abhorrence for manmade borders prohibiting the free movement of people worldwide that cause such tragedies and exploitation isn't directly relevant here, but it was at the peripheries of my mind when writing the story, and led me to wanting something startling at the end, when a truck was opened.

What if the vehicles had ceased to carry water, and were now carrying blood? I realised this would link directly to the themes in 'When the Water Stops' and provide a Northern Hemisphere angle. Considering the UK's history of exploitation, we can only surmise where the blood might be coming from, yet I wanted it to be made clear—almost celebratory at the conclusion from the characters' point of view—that one person's tragedy can become another's lifeline. Having children open the truck absolves them of being complicit in the presumed horror, but also indicates where the future might be heading.

This is madness, surely?

The story itself didn't take long to write. I squeezed out time for two or three sessions. As usual when writing, parallel themes were drawn to the central story in the process of writing it, like iron filings attracted to a magnetised train pulling through the night: the effects of dehydration, the danger of reusing plastic bottles, the idea of substances being *watered down*, the meal I'd cooked the previous evening, the frogs who hibernate and reawaken after rain.

Initially the truck was going to be attacked when Finch and Joel reached the end of the queue, but it felt too simplistic. I wanted a gap to indicate a greater passing of time, how urgencies change.

Switching from Finch to Joel midway created this shift. Thereafter I had my story.

What I find most interesting in the creative process—especially this one, where the initial idea isn't mine—is how art can bloom into existence almost unbidden, that we can consider almost anything and put it in a different light to create something new. That *without* Eugen's calling, this story, these characters, would *never* have come into being.

That's the true power behind artistic works: that they beget and beget and beget. I look forward to reading the other interpretations in this collection, to seeing how the other children of Eugen's story have lapped up the source material.

When the Water Stops, Again

Dominique Hecq

Plantes acaules, rouges, sortent de terre. Puis flambent.

The earth spills blood dust, blood rust, blood ash.

Puits asséché.

Time gorged with death.

Déchirure du ciel.

Une saignée, une excavation, une faille avalant l'horizon fracassé. Déjà enfoui.

Un peuple exsangue.

Détournement de mots.

Fire, dust, drought, Babel.

In 'When the Water Stops' Eugen Bacon has created a fascinating and deeply engrossing fable about a disaster set in Africa that spans light years. The location is apposite: Africa is the so-called cradle of civilisation. But in many ways, this is an allegorical fable about what the human race faces here and now. It could therefore be transposed onto any continent.

The story offers glimpses into a disappearing way of life—indeed into *disappearing life itself*. Climate change catches up with an unnamed people in an unnamed nation state. The consequences are dire. Climate deaths happen at first randomly, then order comes in the guise of power fuelled by fear, and deaths occur in accordance with a sinister plan devised by the leader of the nation and implemented by a man turned scavenger, evoking notorious genocides such as those perpetrated by Hitler, Mussolini and Idi Amin Dada.

This is a cautionary tale about human beings at their most vulnerable, and also at their worst. The disenfranchised are at the mercy of the more powerful, prey to cruelty and heinous crimes. Consider how the Nation State and the Church concur in condoning the 'violation of the principles of humanity' encapsulated in 'three spaced words: I. Can't. Breathe'.

In extremis, people act not to save their loved ones, but their own skin. Theirs is less a bloody battle than a battle of the blood. It is ironic that this precious liquid contains CO_2, the very substance at the core of the climate question. Bodies are bled dry. Souls ignite. Language disintegrates, and Babel rules.

At a time of profound material, geopolitical, social, cultural, moral and spiritual crisis, even when COVID-19 may symbolise something far worse to come. We still do not know what shape the disaster will take, nor its extent. Its emergent presence and looming absence seem to be imbued with a sense of endless deferral. As Paddy Manning recently puts it in *Body Count: How Climate Change Is Killing Us*:

> There is no doubt that the planet is rapidly warming, CO_2 is responsible, and the CO_2 is coming from human activity, especially deforestation and the burning of fossil fuels. But what happens next is

> harder to determine. (Manning 2020, p.17)

Manning's book examines Australia's climate deaths from heat, flood, fire, smoke and disease in a global context. The unanswerable question of 'what happens next' conjures up Maurice Blanchot's words in *The Writing of Disaster*, where he states:

> When the disaster comes upon us, it does not come. The disaster is its imminence, but since the future, as we conceive of it is in the order of lived time, belongs in the disaster, the disaster has always already withdrawn or dissuaded it; there is no time or future for the disaster, just as there is no time or space for its accomplishment. (Blanchot 1995, p.1)

We have lived at the edge of global obliteration for some time; it is imminent, yet it remains in abeyance. It so far exceeds our ability to imagine it. It might already be upon us, but we have no way of *knowing*.

It seems that we have lived on the edge of a disaster of apocalyptic proportions for quite some time. It so far exceeds our ability to comprehend what it might look like, yet commentators such as James Berger have suggested that we have been inhabiting a post-apocalyptic age since the end of the second World War:

> In representations after the second World War, the apocalypse became a matter of retrospection. It had already happened. The world was in ruin, a

> remnant. More destruction could occur, but it could only be more of the same. Nothing more would be revealed. All subsequent, post-apocalyptic destruction would be absolutely without meaning, mere representation. (Berger 2000, p. 390)

Berger draws our attention to the apocalyptic tone that emerged in postructuralist theory, with its emphasis on 'shattering, rupture and the sublime' (390-92). Manifested in language—as in, for example, Derrida's terms trace, erasure, *différance*, and dissemination—theses concepts undermine the idea of stability and bring uncertainty to the fore. They expose language like a membrane that is porous and delicate, subject to tears capable of being re-sewn into new forms that are hybrid and mask-like. On a generic plane, such new forms call to mind speculative fiction and allegory.

Despite the pandemic and global warming, we are unable to read the signs of what the future holds. To write and unwrite disaster seems the only way of containing it. And this is what Eugen Bacon has done, projecting our fears and hopes onto the landscape of speculative fiction where the plagues of climate change materialise as bushfires, dust storms, drought and a tragic and final bleed, undoing her deed in the story's lyrical ending:

> Nostalgia, a great-uncle with empty sacks, an odour of mothballs in his breath, his eyes a fortress against hope.

> You think of this moment, over and over, wishing you and the rest of the world remembered different.

A text is always open to several interpretations. I read the ending of 'When the Water Stops' as a debunking of the idea of teleological truth and of the allegorical mode, whereby events can be interpretated to represent a hidden truth with some moral or political import. The last two lines invite us to ask hitherto unasked questions within the parameters of the truth of fiction, not outside of it. Due to the hybridity Bacon favours in her speculative fictions, these parameters are themselves in flux, intimating randomness and potentiality.

I think back to Nietzsche who, in a book-length essay titled *On the Genealogy of Morals*, suggests that it is neither the study of morals, nor the transcending of morality that is important. What is imperative is the questioning of morality. Though Bacon may ask us to question morality as her fable unfolds, she also cautions us against the caustic effects of nostalgia. She begs us to ask new questions about old tales of disaster.

As I write these words, towering rain clouds gather. A northerly roars. The wind hurls at us tree limbs and corrugated iron sheets from across the street. Magpies run amuck, gargling their throats off. Bats flap their wings, squeaking. A clap of thunder. Pelting rain. I turn the computer off. *Désolée*. Run around the house. Close the windows. Inside the chook house, the birds go quiet.

Huddle.

Stemless, red plants come out of the ground.
Then blaze.
La terre éclabousse en poussière de sang,
rouille de sang, cendre de sang.
Dry well.
Le temps gorgé de mort.
Tearing of the sky.
A bleeding, an excavation, a cleft swallowing
the shattered horizon. Already buried.
A bloodless people.
Misuse of words.
Feu, poussière, sécheresse, Babel.

Works Cited

Berger, James 2000 'Introduction: Twentieth-Century Apocalypse: Forecasts and Aftermaths.' Twentieth Century Literature 46: 4, 377-95.

Blanchot, Maurice 1995 *The Writing of Disaster* (trans A Smock), Lincoln, NE, University of Nebraska Press.

Manning, Paddy 2020 *Body Count: How Climate Change is Killing Us*, Sydney, Simon & Schuster.

Nietzsche, Friedrich 2000 *On the Genealogy of Morals*, in *Basic Works of Nietzsche* (trans W Kaufmann), New York, The Modern Library.

What I See in ‘When the Water Stops’: A Personal Reflection

Clare Rhoden

In the same way that every writer brings their own perspective to a story, so every reader receives the story as an individual. Formal literature curricula, ‘The Canon’ and SparkNotes (2021) study guides notwithstanding, every story reaches each new reader as an individual act of communication.

What you read may not be exactly what I read.

I first met ‘When the Water Stops’ in Eugen Bacon’s short story collection *Danged Black Thing* (2021). The title denotes a devastating piece of futuristic climate fiction. But the short story is more than that. It’s horror, and warning, and history. It’s a story that cradles layers of meaning about some manifestly unpalatable truths.

In its fleeting presence I encountered cautionary words about where the world is heading; horrific descriptions about what the world is like, right now; and a ferocious critique on an abominable past which is not past and never will be.

My reactions to the story arise from individual factors such as my age, gender, culture, experiences and education. My introduction to Anthropocene climate horror came via the seminal *Silent Spring* by Rachel Carson (1962) which I read as a young high school student. At the time I didn't comprehend how controversial Carson's book was. I certainly had no understanding of the profit-driven, calculated reactions of powerful forces in the chemical and agricultural sectors that railed against her. I simply understood that human actions can affect other life forms on our planet, and that poisoning the environment is a bad thing. A simple enough concept, and one that I absorbed whole.

My upbringing in suburban Australia taught me to value water as a scarce resource. Any child who left the tap dripping—let alone running!—would have very sore ears. There was one bathroom in a house of nine, and we ran one bath each day for the whole family, washing in turn from the least-dirty to the most-dirty in a way that respected both cleanliness and economy.

In the dry summer, the cold bathwater was siphoned out via hose onto the garden beds: one day the vegetables, then the flower beds, the next day the water was flushed into shallow channels that my father dug around the dripline of the big trees in our old garden—long since lost to urban density. We allowed the 'lawn' to brown off every summer. It always came back new and green with the autumn rains and, in the winter, puddles arrived for building mud-castles and splashing gum boots. Most winters, there was enough rain to fill the city's dams the following summer.

This is all to say that I grew up with no idea that in other parts of the world, the abundance or scarcity of fresh water was a matter of life and death—not for grassy playgrounds—but for people.

Since those days, much has changed. I know now that my family was very well off, that my country was, and is, very well off. We still run our baths and flush our toilets with drinking-quality water. Who can comprehend such luxury? Today I can bring a lifetime of education and reading to stories such as 'When the Water Stops'.

Let's get back this homing story. The very first sentence skewers the climate crisis:

> *As the climate turned, it hurled at them bushfires that razed huts to the ground, dust storms that swept away families, drought—all the cattle and sheep gone, reduced to skin, then skeletons.*

And the next sentence opens the horror:

> *At first, the villagers took turns on the bleed, sharing dreams and fears, understanding that as a people they were the same.*

The bleed? That two-word hook yanks this story out of what could be conventional climate fiction into a new dreadfulness. In mainstream climate fiction arising from the English-speaking world, we can expect a 'desertified' landscape and a remnant society subsisting on rationed water. Perhaps a fantastic figure arrives with a new way to clean the chemical-poisoned sludge surrounding each continent. Or maybe someone will discover a technological solution that pivots on vast resources of water deep underground, allowing Earth to succour her children. Or there's an off-world solution that involves humans leaping from their desiccated planet to somewhere more promising, Terra-forming some new rock in the cosmos as they were unable to Terra-maintain their own home. In general, climate fiction invites the reader to look at the suffering of Earth's life forms as a prompt to action.

See what we are doing! such stories command the converted—obsessively hand-wringing, miserably head-shaking, accusatorily finger-pointing.

'When the Water Stops' is different, incisively and magnificently so.

Many cli-fi stories depict Earth as a single entity and climate change as a matter that affects us all. Both contentions are true, but Bacon's story shows them to be insufficient. Climate change does not fall equally on Earth's children, and not merely by accidents of geography. We're now more aware, for example, of the threat of rising sea levels to the island nations of the Pacific. But the thrust of 'When the Water Stops' is not about altitude; it's about poverty and exploitation.

Now the stark bones of the story's historical substructure start to show. Try these razor-sharp sentences:

> *When the water stops, the blood must flow, says the woman with a rainbow*

diamond shaped into a bangle around her wrist...

She flourishes from the catastrophe of others. Blooms on the unimportant. ***Like the people in her cellar, beggars from the village.*** Theirs is a narrative she doesn't believe in...*

She cradles with affection a labradoodle puppy to her breast.

(*My bold)

From the rainbow diamond to the labradoodle puppy, the narrative wades with its head held high above the piteous groaning of the oppressed, the enslaved, the exploited, the dying. Those with no choices. As a reader, I have to look that rich urban woman in the face and contemplate the mirror image she flaunts at me. It's not a joyful task.

The story rounds out back in the village, picking apart the family of hopeful youngsters, consigning value to them as substances of others' survival. Humans as commodities. I hear echoes of Jonathan Swift's famous satire *A Modest Proposal* (1729), which recommends that the impoverished Irish sell their children to the rich as foodstuffs: if the only harvest the native Irish can successfully produce are children, why not fashion them into a specialty crop that's easy to grow and delicious to eat?

There is, however, less deadpan and more focus on the human cost of endless economic growth in Bacon's tale. The author shows us more individual compassion for the worn-out mother and the motherless little ones. More outright exposition of the failings of self-styled Great Leaders, across the globe, across the centuries.

As I read it, the story functions as both cautionary parable and plaintive refrain. 'When the Water Stops' is about the Third World and the dark history of slavery that underpins the First World, that arguably has enabled the First World. It's about the haves and the have-nots. It's about selflessness and its opposite: the human propensity to ignore and disbelieve the suffering of others in order to prosper oneself, or just to continue one's comfortable lifestyle. Altruism dies of thirst while egotism flourishes.

The story is also about the power of narrative to reflect the world while teasing us with story.

And it picks at my brain with the persistence of a dripping tap, telling me that something is horribly wrong…

And you, dear reader, what do you see?

Works Cited

Bacon, Eugen 2021, *Danged Black Thing*, Transit Lounge Publishing, Melbourne

Carson, Rachel 1962, *Silent Spring,* Houghton Mifflin Harcourt, Boston Massachusetts

SparkNotes 2021, website, viewed 21 November 2021, available at <https://www.sparknotes.com>

Swift, Jonathan 2005 (first published 1729), *Gulliver's Travels/A modest proposal*, Simon & Schuster, New York

Behind the Water

Eugen Bacon

Our Earth is not well. Scientists won't stop harping about it, they won't, long after the water stops and we are extinct as dinosaurs, existing only as fossils. Like prophets of doom in howls that are sometimes sombre, sometimes emotional, they tell us and tell us to heed the signs of falling. Stained fresh air. The last milk of human kindness. Empty. Empty. Empathy folded, again, again. Counting time, time… in extra droughts, escalating temperatures, melting glaciers, wilder weather. Are those sturdier hurricanes, more relentless heat waves?

Each day is emulation, a re-enactment of our last rites in patterns of behaviour that refuse to be expunged. The animals come in two by two (walrus/ unicorn/manticore): where is the ark? Roll slim cigarettes. Celebrate mass.

Massacre is calling.

When I wrote 'When the Water Stops', an experimental story, I wanted to encapsulate multi-voiced narratives, shifting perspectives, that spoke, told us… what happens when water is so scarce that we must extract it from blood.

But whose?

I wanted to write a black speculative story so stark and startling in its gaze at women and children in the village, someone might notice.

It was writing that was a curiosity, a search, a warning, a lament… I wanted to bring it out in a myriad of identities that reflected hybridity, collision, transformation, longing. I wrote it in the heart of shifting events on the matter of Black Lives Matter—it was inevitable there would be a leader of the nation pushing out his lip, standing on the steps of a shrine and holding, holding an upturned bible as cameras flashed and riot police fell with batons, rubber bullets and gas masks upon agreeable activists.

When I perform this story at conferences and events, I accompany the reading with grotesque illustrations of excess destined to shock. Vivid images of water droplets, crimson in a splash drip. Cartoon caricatures of the leader of the nation and the rich woman in the metropolis killing people in her cellar— *Turn off the sound of their groaning!* she snaps to her servants, as she clutches to her breast a labradoodle puppy.

A black man holding his head in trepidation of what he has done to his village wife, and the fourteen ravenous children that are, for him, options.

An image of Afia, a hungry-looking child, furious at the world, as his brother or companion peers with unhappy eyes across his shoulder.

Skeletal children, big-eyed, bones sticking out of ribs, reminiscent of the photos we saw of a famine-stricken Ethiopia—now the youngest child speaks.

A long silence generally follows each reading, then questions stammer out.

In *Languages of Water*, I contemplated the invisible reader of this climate change story that wrote the 'other'. I wondered what each reader might bring in their unique interpretation of the story. What if the story existed in different forms of itself? Different languages: Swahili, French, Malay… Different inhabitations: flash fiction, poetry, short stories...

The 'homing story' endows a certain significance of the text to its core players—aligned with Gérard Genette's 'paratexts' of interpretation (1997, pp. 2–3), liminal devices and conventions, within and without a book, that form part of the complex mediation between the book, its author, its publisher and its reader. The original 'When the Water Stops' paves the way, but each core player in the literary act charts their own steps.

Perhaps my biggest fascination or conflict in the story's destabilisation was seeing the genesis of new(er) stories, birthed from the homing story. Andrew Hook's 'So Close to Home', Clare Rhoden's 'Handsome Fox Thirsts for More', Clara Chow's 'New(er) Water, Erin Latimer's 'Deeper Still', Tamantha Smith's 'Old Water'… Then I fell instantly and tearfully in love with Quyên Nguyễn-Hoàng's powerfully unique hybrid—a short story/poem replica in a conjoined twin: 'New Winds' and its Vietnamese translation 'Gió Mới'. And then Audrey Chin's Malay translation, another ingenious hybrid with its monochrome illustrations... In studying these artistic interpretations, I began to see firsthand how things are made and unmade, how my own 'subjectivity is immersed and dissolved' (Barthes 1985, p. 105).

I saw language as play inside the dirge of a broken world. I thought back to the French literary theorist, critic and philosopher Roland Barthes and his *le plaisir du texte* (1975), the alignment of literary writing with creative play—and what he describes in *The Grain of the Voice* (1985) as a 'blissful enjoyment of fabrication and function' (p. 104).

The concept behind *Languages of Water* borrows from Barthes' pleasure of writing and pleasure of reading, his enchantment of unique articulation, where the author is the text's very first reader. But that same author is unable to contain their creation. The birth of a new reader, once the work steps out of the author's dialectical space, is at the death of the author (Barthes 1977, pp. 148).

Languages of Water extends the dialectical space of a single writer in its invitation to other writers to offer the reader a differential experience, to engage the reader in the 'other' writer's own idea of play. A writerly pleasure of writing.

I understood how Barthes' context of text as a marriage of writings lauds the non-originality of text, its interdependence with other texts, whereby a text is a multi-dimensional space and writers only assemble, pre-mix, borrow from, draw upon… that which is already written. Where, according to Barthes, a text is approached, is experienced, is plural, is metonymic (1977, pp. 158–159). Text is a *social space* that leaves no language safe (p. 164).

Ah, translations.

But how much do we let go? As a speaker of both Swahili and English, I could not help but jump in to 'fix' the Swahili translation, where I perceived that the translator might have missed my intent.

Where my story read:

C02 may induce dizziness, tiredness, restlessness, convulsions or coma...

The translation read:

Loss of water in the body in the body *may induce...*

#

Where my story read:

But still they were not strong enough to take another turn when it arrived.

The translation read:

But still they were not strong enough ***to think beyond where they had reached****.*

#

Where my story read:

Like the people in her cellar, *beggars from the village.*

The translation read:

Like the people of her kind, you won't believe, beggars come *from the village.*

#

Where my story read:

They [the people from the village] are mistakes, *awkward memories that float a different image every time...*

The translation read:

It was a mistake, *awkward memories that float a different image every time...*

#

I could see how the text rendered itself open to both language interpretations. I meddled, refined the translation to my inherent meaning. Why could I not let go, and allow the destabilisation of the text in its translated form?

Sometimes a language translation insists to know or to consider the character's gender. If one said, *Oh, I thought Afia was a girl*, and I said, *Afia can be anything you want!*—in English it might not matter that much. But in French nouns have a gender: they can be masculine (masculine) or feminine (féminin), so it matters bloody much.

One translator offered to do a Cantonese translation of the Chinese translation of the English version of the homing story. But I thought back to a game we used to play as children, called the broken telephone. We would sit in a row, then the first child would whisper a single word—intentionally long and obscure—into the ear of the second child. The second child would whisper the word, as they heard it, into the ear of the third child, and so forth, until the last child finally blurted out the result. It was hilarious to discover a simple word that started off as 'crocodile' might morph and riven to shore up as 'carbon of the Nile', or something far more ludicrous.

The whisperer would deliberately mislead the listener, first ominously breathing into the listener's ear, and then growling the word with intentional loss of accuracy, for the chortling glee of hearing the gnarled construction at the end of the broken telephone.

I worried about the translation from a translation. Perhaps a broken telephone conveying accidental 'misinterpretation' from a translation already splintered. Where was my trust, my letting go—why was the author refusing to die, as in Barthes' death of the author, and allow for the reader's birthing?

But in other ways I stood back.

In *Languages of Water*, and the story in different forms of itself, I taught myself to resist the idea of text as a stable, fixed self, and allowed other players to destabilise it in patterns of multiplicity—as philosopher Gilles Deleuze and his collaborator psychoanalyst Felix Guattari explored in *A Thousand Plateaus* (1987). So the homing story 'When the Water Stops' represents Deleuze and Guattari's rhizome that has no beginning or end. It is between things, interbeing.

Intermezzo.

And our Earth is still not well. Must we wait until the water stops?

Works Cited

Bacon, Eugen 2021, 'When the Water Stops', *Fantasy Magazine,* Columbia.

Barthes, Roland 1975, *The pleasure of the text*, trans. Richard Miller, Hill and Wang, New York.

Barthes, Roland 1977, 'The Death of the Author', trans. Stephen Heath in *Image,*

Music, Text, Fontana, London, pp. 142–148.

Barthes, Roland 1985, *The Grain of the Voice*, University of California Press, California.

Deleuze, Gilles & Guattari, Felix 1987, *A Thousand Plateaus*, trans. Brian Massumi, University of Minnesota Press, Minneapolis.

Genette, Gérard 1997, *Paratexts: Thresholds of Interpretation*, Cambridge University Press, New York.

When the Water Stops (Bengali)

Sudeep Chatterjee

জল ফুরিয়ে গেলে

পরিবেশ বদলে যাচ্ছিল। এই পরিবর্তনের পরিণাম তাদের ওপর নিক্ষিপ্ত হল অচিরেই। ঝোপের আগুন থেকে বেড়ে ওঠা দাবানল কুঁড়েঘরগুলোকে গ্রাস করে মাটিতে মিশিয়ে দিল, ধুলোর ঝড়ে ভেসে গেল কত কত পরিবার, আর ছিল খরা— সমস্ত গবাদি পশু আর ভেড়ার দল নিশ্চিহ্ন হয়ে গেল সে খরায়। শীর্ণকায় হতে হতে শুধু চামড়াটাই রয়ে গিয়েছিল তাদের, একসময় তারা ক্রমে কঙ্কালে পরিণত হল। প্রথম দিকে গ্রামের মানুষগুলো পালা করে পরস্পরের রক্তের ভাগ পাচ্ছিল, পাশাপাশি তারা ভাগ করে নিচ্ছিল নিজেদের স্বপ্ন ও শঙ্কাও। তারা বুঝেছিল, মানুষ হিসেবে তারা সবাই এক।

কিন্তু একজন সাধারণ প্রাপ্তবয়স্ক পুরুষের শরীরে রক্তের পরিমাণ মাত্র পাঁচ লিটার— সেখান থেকে চল্লিশ শতাংশ হ্রাস পাওয়া মানে মৃত্যু অবশ্যম্ভাবী। প্রান্তসীমায় থাকা উনচল্লিশ শতাংশে জলের মাত্রা মাত্র বিরানব্বই শতাংশ, বাকিটা ধুয়ে যায় গ্লুকোজ, হরমোন, প্রোটিন, চর্বি, ভিটামিন, খনিজ লবণ এবং কার্বন ডাই অক্সাইডে— তাতে আর লাভ কোনটুকু? কার্বন ডাই অক্সাইডের উপস্থিতি বেড়ে গেলে মাথা ঘোরা, ক্লান্তি, অস্থিরতা বা খিঁচুনি ঘটা খুবই স্বাভাবিক, কোমায় চলে যাওয়াও অসম্ভব নয়। এই সমস্ত যোগ বিয়োগের পর, একজন মানুষের শরীরের রক্ত থেকে সারা গাঁয়ের জন্য আর কোনটুকু জল পাওয়া যায়?

এই প্রশ্নটা তাদের সকলের মাথায় ঘুরপাক খাচ্ছিল। এদিকে যে সমস্ত স্বেচ্ছাসেবীরা গাঁয়ের মানুষের খাতিরে শরীরের রক্ত দিয়েছিল, তারা পরবর্তী চার থেকে আট সপ্তাহ ধরে ফণীমনসার পাতা ও রস চুষে চলল, খেয়ে চলল ডুমুর

আর মরুভূমির পিঁপড়েও। কিন্তু তবুও, তাদের পালা আসার আগে পর্যন্ত কেউই পর্যাপ্ত সামর্থ্য অর্জন করতে পারল না। রক্তাল্পতা পূরণ করা কোনোমতেই সম্ভব হল না তাদের পক্ষে।

ফলে পরিস্থিতি বদলে গেল। যারা আগে স্বেচ্ছায় রক্ত দিতে রাজি হয়েছিল, এইবার তারা কাঠি টেনে সেই সিদ্ধান্ত নিতে বাধ্য হল— স্রেফ ভাগ্য, অথবা দুর্ভাগ্যও বলা চলে! একটা কাঠি, তার ওপর কোনও জোরাজুরি চলে না। বড় হলে বড়, ছোট হলে ছোট। তুমি ছোট কাঠিটা টানলেই তোমার অদৃষ্টে সীলমোহর পড়ে গেল।মৃত্যুর পরোয়ানা লিখে দেওয়া হল তোমার নামে। একমাত্র সান্ত্বনা হল, তোমার এই মৃত্যু একাকী হবে না, বরং এই মৃত্যু এক সমষ্টিগত উৎসব হয়ে উঠবে। সমাজের চাহিদা মেটানোর উৎসব।

কিন্তু একসময় জীবনের বাজি রেখে কাঠি টানার এই চলও থেমে গেল। স্বেচ্ছায় নিজের জীবন উৎসর্গ করতে আর কে চায়? ফলে আজকাল বিষয়টি ঠিক করার ভার পড়েছে বিত্তবান মানুষের ওপর, যাদের হাতে থাকা প্রতিটা কাঠিই হল লম্বা। তারাই ঠিক করে দেয়, গণহত্যার জন্য কাদের বেছে নেওয়া হবে? তারাই ঠিক করবে, কাদের দেহের ছাই বাতাসে উড়ে যাবে? রূপক হিসেবেই লিখেছিলাম সন্দেহ নেই, কিন্তু ঘটনাটা বাস্তবেই ঘটে গেল ভাঁটিখানায়।

ভাঁটিখানার সেই মহিলা

এই সপ্তাহে তার একটাই কাজ। একটা পাত্রের মধ্যে বসে থাকা, ঠিক যেখানে নরম আগুনের আঁচ জ্বলছে। সে আচ্ছন্ন হয়ে আছে স্মৃতির আসা যাওয়ায়, সব কিছুই মন্থর গতিতে চলছে তার মাথায়। যখন সে এই সময়টার কথা মনে করবে, কী মনে পড়বে তার? সে দেখছে ধোঁয়াগুলো তাকে সোহাগে জড়িয়ে ধরে ঘুরছে, দৈত্যাকার মেঘের শব্দে অস্পষ্ট হয়ে উঠছে কথাগুলো: তুমি এখন কোথায়? তার

আত্মা আজ আকাশের উজ্জ্বলতম বস্তু। আজ, সে রক্তদাতা। আগামীকাল হল আকাঙ্খা।

রাষ্ট্রের নেতা

দশ বছর আগে, এক বড় নেতা তার আশ্রয়স্থল ছেড়ে বেরিয়ে আসেন। পোপের উদ্দেশ্যে জাদুঘর হিসাবে খোলা মন্দিরের ধাপগুলি দখল করার জন্য দৃঢ়প্রতিজ্ঞ ছিলেন তিনি। মানবাধিকার কর্মী, কয়েকটি উচ্চ আদালত এবং অসংখ্য মায়েরা হতবাক রয়ে গিয়েছিল যখন তিনি ক্যামেরার ঝলকানির সামনে গোটা এক মিনিট ধরে হাতে বাইবেল তুলে ধরে কথা বলে গেলেন। ব্যাটন, রবার বুলেট আর গ্যাস মাস্ক পরিহিত দাঙ্গা নিরোধক পুলিশ স্নেহ ও ভালোবাসার স্লোগান দেওয়া শান্তিপূর্ণ বিক্ষোভকারীদের ওপর চড়াও হল। অর্থনীতি যখন নাগরিক অস্থিরতাকে টপকে গিয়েছে আর শেয়ার মার্কেট চড়চড় করে উঠছে, তখন আর এক ফোঁটা রক্তের কী গুরুত্ব থাকে? খেয়াল করেছ, ডাও ২৬৭ পয়েন্ট উঠেছে? আর ন্যাসড্যাক কম্পোজিট কোথায় পৌঁছেছে দেখেছ? বিবর্তনবাদের তত্ত্বটিই তো প্রাকৃতিক নির্বাচনের এমন এক ফর্ম নিয়ে যা নিজের সর্বাধিক প্রতিলিপি তৈরি করতে সমর্থ হবে?

আলোকবর্ষ দূরে অবস্থিত, বিকল্প মহাবিশ্বের প্রতিটা আর্চবিশপ, উপাসনার জন্য ব্যবহৃত পদ্ধতির অপব্যবহারের দ্বারা ক্ষুব্ধ হয়ে উঠবে, মানবতার নীতির ঐতিহাসিক লঙ্ঘনের বিবেচনা করে মাত্র কয়েকটা ফাঁকা শব্দ উচ্চারণ করবে তারা। আমি। নিশ্বাস। নিতে পারছি না।

প্রতিবাদের চেহারা চিরকাল কুৎসিতই হয়, নেতাটি ভাবলেন। আর সামনে আবার নির্বাচনও আসছে।

মহানগরের ধনী মহিলা

যখন জল ফুরিয়ে যাবে, রক্তকে কিন্তু বয়ে যেতে হবে তখনও। কব্জিতে ইন্দ্রধনুষী হীরের আকৃতির চুড়ি পরিহিত মহিলাটি জানালেন। একটা বিলিয়ন ডলার ব্রোচ— একটা অরোরা দুলের সেট— দূর সম্পর্কের এক কাকার মাসতুতো ভাইয়ের পিসতুতো ভাই এই উপহারটি দিয়েছিল, যার নাম তিনি চেষ্টা করেও মনে করতে পারলেন না। নামধাম মনে রাখা খুবই কঠিন কাজ।

এই মহিলার সমৃদ্ধির চাবিকাঠি হল অন্যদের বিপর্যয়, গুরুত্বহীন মানুষের মৃতশয্যার ওপর পা রেখে প্রস্ফুটিত হয় তার জীবন। ভূমিগত সেলারের লোকজন, গ্রামের ভিক্ষুক...এই লোকগুলোর বানিয়ে বলা গল্পে তিনি মোটেও বিশ্বাস করেন না, এই ধরনের গল্প শুধু শিল্পের সমঝদারদের কাছে রক্ষিত পুরোনো ছবিতেই প্রতিফলিত হয়। যে রাজনীতির হাত ধরে হিটলার, মুসোলিনি আর ইদি আমিন দাদার উত্থান, এই মহিলার অন্তরও আসলে সেই একই রাজনীতির উপাদান দিয়ে তৈরি। তিনি মনেপ্রাণে বিশ্বাস করেন, প্রায় নিঁখুত ভবিষ্যতের প্রতিচ্ছবিতে ওই চাষাভূষো লোকগুলোর জায়গা নেই, তাতে আর তিনি কী করতে পারেন? এরা আসলে ভ্রান্ত মানুষ! যখনই তিনি চোখ তুলে তাকান, বিচ্ছিরি স্মৃতির মতো বিভিন্ন রূপ নিয়ে চোখের সামনে ঘুরে বেড়ায় তারা, কিন্তু কখনও বাস্তব আকার ধারণ করে না। মানবতা সম্পর্কে কত বইই তো আছে, কিন্তু এখানে ওই পদ্ধতি কাজ করে না। এ বড় কঠিন ঠাঁই।

"ওদের এই গোঙানির শব্দ থামাও!" তার চাকরদের ওপর গর্জে ওঠেন মহিলা। হাহাকারের এই ক্রন্দনধ্বনি কখনও পুরোপুরি সাদা বা কালো হয়ে ওঠে না, সুরবিন্যাস বা কম্পোজিশনের নিয়মও পালন করে না। এই কান্নার ভিতরে যদি কোনও প্রশ্ন লুকিয়ে থাকে, সেই প্রশ্নের ভাষা 'ব্যাবেল' ছাড়া কিছু নয়। কিছু অস্পষ্ট স্বর ও শব্দ ছাড়া তাতে কিছুই নেই। এই ভাষায় নিহিত অক্ষর, স্বরবর্ণ, বাক্য গঠন, উপমা বা প্রসঙ্গ তিনি বুঝে উঠতে পারেন না, আর চেষ্টা করাও অসম্ভব। এ এক অসম্ভব কঠিন ব্যাপার।

সহজ জিনিসের কিন্তু অভাব নেই। কেবলমাত্র নাক ব্যবহার করেই ভালো মদের বিচার করা যায়। ভিনটেজ প্রোডিউস, যা সস্তায় গ্রাম থেকে নিয়ে আসা হয়। গ্রামের মানুষের খাঁটি রক্ত দিয়ে তৈরি মদ, দূষণজনিত কোনও সংক্রমণ তাতে নেই। তামার পাত্রে রাখা স্মোকড বেকন আর গোলমরিচ থেকে উঠে আসা মিষ্টি সুবাসিত ধোঁয়া মিশে যায় সঠিক অম্লতা বজায় রাখা গ্রামের রক্তের সঙ্গে।

তার প্রজাতিকে বাঁচিয়ে রাখতে হলে এই ভিনটেজ রক্তকে বয়ে যেতে হবে। পরম স্নেহে তিনি তার ল্যাব্রাডুডল কুকুরছানাকে তুলে নিয়ে বুকে জড়িয়ে ধরেন।

<u>এক চিন্তাগ্রস্ত বিবাহিত পুরুষ</u>

বিপ্লব এসেছিল, যখন সে যুক্তির কথাটা উল্লেখ করেছিল।

তিনটে শুকনো কাসাভা বিস্কুট আর চোদ্দটি ক্ষুধার্ত মুখের প্রতিফলন আপনা থেকেই সেই যুক্তিটা তৈরি করে দিয়েছিল। এই যুক্তিই তাকে প্রশ্ন করতে বাধ্য করেছিল: স্ত্রী না সন্তান? সন্তানদের অস্তিত্বে এনেছে তো তার স্ত্রীই। যে জীবনচক্র তারা শুরু করেছিল তার চেয়ে যন্ত্রণাদায়ক আর কী হতে পারে?

হয়তো তার কাছে নির্দয় হওয়ার জন্য একটা অজুহাতও ছিল। প্রতিদিনের ঘৃণা, বিরক্তি আর অনুশোচনা বামন বানরের মতো তার মনে চুপিসাড়ে ঢুকে ঘাঁটি গেড়েছিল এবং পরে সেগুলোই চুরি, ছিনতাই জাতীয় পতঙ্গবত স্বভাবে পরিণত হয়েছিল। একটা হতাশাজনক বিয়ের পরবর্তীতে তার কাছে যে বিষয়গুলো এসেছিল, সেই নিয়ে ক্ষোভ ধরে রাখার মতো মানুষ সে ছিল না, ফলে এটাই বলা ঠিক হবে যে তার নেওয়া সিদ্ধান্তের পিছনে যে অনুভূতিটা কাজ করত, সেটা হল

ভয়। যখন সেই বৈপ্লবিক সিদ্ধান্ত নেওয়ার পালা যখন তার স্ত্রীর কাছে এল-- স্বামী না সন্তান?--তার মনে কোনও সংশয় ছিল না।

কাজটা তার স্বামীই ঘটিয়েছিল। ঠিক আছে! সে দুঃখিত! কিন্তু লোকে বলে ভাঁটিখানার ব্যাপারটা খুব দ্রুতই ঘটে গিয়েছিল।

তার অনুতাপের কথা জানানোর জন্য সঙ্গে আর কেউ ছিল না, কিন্তু এখন ক্ষুধার্ত সন্তানগুলোকে খাওয়ানোর জন্য পর্যাপ্ত অর্থ অবশ্যই ছিল। সবচেয়ে ছোট বাচ্চাটির বয়স মাত্র দু' বছর, শুক্রবারে জন্ম নেওয়া আফিয়া। আবিম্বোলা, যে ধনীর সন্তান হয়েও সর্বদা গরীব হয়েই রইল। আমারা, লাবণ্যময়ী ছোট্ট বাচ্চাটি এখন ফোলা পেট নিয়ে ঘুরে বেড়ায়, কোয়াশিওরকরের ফলে ওর মাথার চুলগুলো সব উঠে গেছে। চি, কে, রে, পো-র কথাও বলতে হয়, নাইলনের চুল আর চোখের কোণে বালি ভর্তি করে থাকা দু' জোড়া যমজ সন্তান।

এইসব সে করতে পেরেছে, স্ত্রীর যাওয়ার পরেই... চোদ্দটি বিকল্প কিন্তু তার কাছে এখনও খোলা।

<u>আফিয়া, চোদ্দজন মাতৃহীনদের মধ্যে পঞ্চম</u>

আমি ফোস্কা ওঠা রাস্তায় পড়ে থাকা ফাটা ডিম। কাঁটাতারের জালে জড়িয়ে যাওয়া মরণাসন্ন পাখি। শেয়ালটা এদিক পানে এগিয়ে আসছে, দুলকি চালে এগিয়ে আসছে... আমাকে খাবে বলে। আবার সেই নস্টালজিয়া ফিরে এসেছে আমার! স্কুল নয়, স্যুপ নয়, শুধু ফিসফিসিয়ে বাঁশি বাজানো শূন্য আকাশ যেখানে আমরা মৃতদের কবর দিই। আমি একটি চিহ্নিত কার্ড - লাল দাগে রাঙা। শুকনো ঝর্ণার

চোখে তীর ছুটবে এইবার। তুমি কি আমার মা? ব্ল্যাক মাম্বার হিসহিসানিতে আটকে গিয়েছে একটি কঙ্কাল। ভুল পথে ঘুরে মরছে ধূসর পালক।

<u>সবচেয়ে ছোট্ট শিশুটি কথা বলেছে</u>

আমি এমন কিছুর সন্ধানে আছি যা সম্পর্কে আমি নিজেই জানি না। একটা হাত আর একটা চাহনি, একটি হাসি ও একটা গন্ধ। এখানে একরকম আরাম আছে, উষ্ণতা আছে। আমার মনে নেই সেই মুখটির কথা যে আসে আর চলে যায়, চলে যায় ভালোবাসায় ফাটল ধরিয়ে। খুব জটিল এই জায়গাটা, নিরাপদও নয়। অস্পষ্ট এবং ভেঙে টুকরো টুকরো হওয়া পাথর ছড়িয়ে আছে সব জায়গায়।

নস্টালজিয়া, বড় জ্যাঠা যে খালি বস্তা নিয়ে ঘুরে বেড়ায়, তার নিঃশ্বাস থেকে মিটবলের গন্ধ ভেসে আসে, তার চোখ যেন সমস্ত আশাকে আটকে রেখেছে দুর্গের মতো।। এই মুহূর্তটির কথা বারবার মনে ঘুরপাক খায়। আর চায় যে পৃথিবী আলাদাভাবে মনে রাখুক।

Acknowledgement

'Black Queen' was first published in *Earth Day 2022*, April 2022

'Thingo' was first published in *Other Terrain*, August 2019

'When the Water Stops' was first published in *The Magazine of Fantasy & Science Fiction*, May/June 2021

About The Authors

Aldegunda Matoyo is a Tanzanian working in capital markets and securities. She shuttles between the capital city Dodoma and Dar-es-salaam. She is a member of the Tanzania Personal Secretaries Association and is pursuing a degree in Secretarial Studies at the Tanzania Public Service College. Miss Matoyo has been involved in the public education programmes countrywide, giving knowledge to the public and making capital markets in Tanzania known, encouraging understandings on how to learn to invest in financial markets.

She loves music, travelling, wine, her sweet daughter Ashley and family. Her Swahili is the sound of music, and her laughter a playful river on its way to dance with the lake.

Andrew Hook is a European writer who has been published extensively in the independent press since 1994 in a variety of genres, with over 160 short stories in print, including notable appearances in *Interzone*, *Black Static*, and several anthologies from PS Publishing and NewCon Press. His fiction has been reprinted in anthologies including *Best British Horror 2015* and *Best British Short Stories 2020*, has been shortlisted for British Fantasy Society awards, and he was longlisted for the Commonwealth Writers Short Story Prize in 2020. As editor/publisher, he has won three British Fantasy Society awards and he also has been a judge for the World Fantasy Awards. Most recent publications include *Candescent Blooms* (Salt Publishing)—5-star reviewed in the Telegraph, several noir crime novels through Head Shot Press, a novella written in collaboration with the legendary San Francisco art collective known as The Residents, and his seventh short story collection, *Frequencies of Existence* (NewCon Press). Co-written with Eugen Bacon, the novel *Secondhand Daylight* will be published in 2023. He can be found at www.andrew-hook.com or @AndrewHookUK

Audrey Chin is a Southeast Asian writer whose work explores the intersections between gender, faith and culture. Her essays, short stories, novels and contemplative verses have been published in Singapore, India, the UK and the US. She is a Fellow of the 2017 International Writers Program in Iowa. Find out more at www.audreychin.com

Cheng Tim Tim is a poet and teacher from Hong Kong, currently based between Edinburgh and London. Her pamphlet *Tapping at Glass* is forthcoming in 2023. Her poems are published or anthologised in *POETRY*, *The Rialto*, *Ambit*, *Cicada*, *Our Time is a Garden*, and elsewhere. Her latest appearances include the Hidden Door festival, and Loop, BBC Scotland. timtimcheng.com

Clara Chow is the author of three story collections *Dream Storeys, Modern Myths* (shortlisted for the 2020 Singapore Literature Prize) and *Not Great, But At Least Something*, two travelogues *New Orleans and Caves* and a bilingual poetry collection *几首烂情诗/Lousy Love Poems*. Having started her career in journalism, she now runs tiny indie Hermit Press.

Clare Rhoden started writing as a youngster, and hasn't stopped. She lives in Melbourne Australia with her husband and super smart poodle-cross. She enjoys reruns of old Dr Who and Star Trek, but who doesn't?

Her dystopian trilogy The Chronicles of the Pale tells of intelligent canini living alongside human tribes on the ruined land. Her WWI historical novel is *The Stars in the Night*, and you can find her short fiction in Overland magazine and several anthologies. Clare writes about culture, legends and history, and about dreams. See more at clarerhoden.com

David Carlin is a writer of Scottish and English heritage living on unceded Wurrundjeri Woi Wurrung country. He has published seven books, most recently the collaborative *The After-Normal: Brief, Alphabetical Essays on a Changing Planet* (2019) and *100 Atmospheres: Studies in Scale and Wonder* (2019), as well as award-winning creative nonfiction, and previously worked as a writer/director in film, theatre and circus. David is Professor at RMIT University, where he co-founded the non/fictionLab and WrICE, and co-President of the NonfictioNOW Conference.

Dominique Hecq grew up in the French-speaking part of Belgium. She now lives in Melbourne. She writes across genres and sometimes across tongues. Her works include a novel, five collections of short stories and twelve books of poetry. *Kaosmos* (2020), *Tracks* (2020) and *After Cage* (2022) are her latest poetry offerings. With Eugen Bacon, she also co-authored *Speculate* (2021), a collection of microlit. *Smacked & Other Stories of Addiction* is off the press. Among other honours, Dominique is the recipient of The Melbourne Fringe Festival Award for Outstanding Writing and Performance, The New England Review Prize for Poetry, The Martha Richardson Medal for Poetry, the inaugural AALITRA Prize for Literary Translation (Spanish into English) and the 2018 International Best Poets Prize administered by the

International Poetry Translation and Research Centre in conjunction with the International Academy of Arts and Letters.

E. Don Harpe has had a varied career, from military service in the 1960s to industrial engineering. He is a published Nashville songwriter and a real descendant of the Harpe Brothers, America's first serial killers. Harpe has nearly forty short stories, including two in the *Twisted Tales II* anthology that won the Eppie Award for best science fiction anthology in 2007. Harpe lives in South Central Georgia, USA, and devotes his time to his family and his writing.

Erin Latimer is a queer Australian-American writer living on Gadigal land. She studied Creative Writing and Film at the University of New South Wales. Her fiction work has a focus on queer experience, relationships, the future, technology, and sometimes a little bit of magic.

Twitter: @erinwrites.

Eugen Bacon is African Australian—her books *Ivory's Story*, *Danged Black Thing* and *Saving Shadows* are finalists in the British Science Fiction Association (BSFA) Awards. She's a 2022 World Fantasy Award finalist, and was twice announced in the honor list of the Otherwise Awards.

Eugen's creative work has appeared in literary and speculative fiction publications worldwide, including *Award Winning Australian Writing*, BSFA, Fantasy Magazine, Fantasy & Science Fiction, and *Year's Best African Speculative Fiction*. In 2022: *Mage of Fools* (novel), *Chasing Whispers* (short stories) and *An Earnest Blackness* (essays).

Web: eugenbacon.com / Twitter: @EugenBacon

Francesca Rendle-Short is an award-winning novelist, memoirist, and essayist. Her writing pays attention to form, a practice that is experimental, idiosyncratic, attentive to whimsy and transgression. Her research focuses on ethical enquiry, queer thinking, trans-national literatures and literary practices, and the value of collaboration and community building. Her five books include *The Near and the Far* (Vol I and II) and *Bite Your Tongue*. She is Professor of Creative Writing at RMIT in the School of Media and Communication, co-founder of non/fictionLab and WrICE.

Jill Jones is a poet and writer who was born in Sydney and currently works in Adelaide, Australia. Her work has been widely published in most of the leading literary periodicals in Australia as well as in a number of print and online magazines in New Zealand, Canada, the USA, Britain, the Czech Republic, France and India. Her poems have been translated into Chinese, Italian, Spanish, French, Czech and Dutch.

Kyongmi Park (b. 1956) is a second-generation Korean living and writing in Tokyo. Her books include an essay collection, *There Are Always Birds in the Air* (2004) and the translations of Gertrude Stein and Mother Goose. Her latest poetry collection is *Go, Alone* (2021). This poem is from *Tales of Everywhere* (2013). Her work has been translated into Korean, English, Spanish, Serbian, Macedonian and Italian.

Nicki Bacon is a post-teen who still loves partying, exercise and hanging out with mates. He sometimes trains for triathlons and does some acting when he gets casting roles.

Nuzo Onoh is a Nigerian-British writer of speculative fiction. She is a pioneer of the African horror literary subgenre. Hailed as the "Queen of African Horror".

Nuzo holds a Law degree and a Masters degree in Writing, both from Warwick University, United Kingdom. She is also a certified Civil Funeral Celebrant, licensed to conduct non-religious burial services. An avid musician with an addiction to JungYup and K-indie music, Nuzo plays both the guitar and piano, and holds an NVQ in Digital Music Production from City College, Coventry. She currently resides in The West Midlands, UK, with her cat, Tinkerbell.

Oz Hardwick is a European poet, photographer, occasional musician, and academic, whose work has been widely published in international journals and anthologies. He has published nine full collections and chapbooks, including *Learning to Have Lost* (Canberra: IPSI, 2018) which won the 2019 Rubery International Book Award for poetry, and most recently the prose poetry sequence *Wolf Planet* (Clevedon: Hedgehog, 2020). He has also edited or co-edited several anthologies, including *The Valley Press Anthology of Prose Poetry* (Scarborough: Valley Press, 2019) with Anne Caldwell. Oz is Professor of Creative Writing at Leeds Trinity University (UK).

Pandora (b. 1974) was a blogger in the years 2006-2011. She pioneered the compilation of two anthologies of Myanmar women poets in 2012 and 2016. She has published one story book and two collections of poems. Her book Khru Pyit Launcher, published by the Era Publication, won the National Literature Award 2019 for Poetry and S.E.A Write award 2020 for poetry. Pandora is an alumna of the University of Iowa International Writing Program (Fall 2012). She participated in the Taipei Poetry Festival 2017.

Quyên Nguyễn-Hoàng is a poet and translator born in Vietnam. Her work has appeared in *Poetry*, the *Margins*, *Columbia Journal* and other venues. Nguyễn-Hoàng's latest publications include Masked Force (Sàn Art), a bilingual pamphlet on the war photographs of Võ An Khánh, and *Chronicles of a Village* (Penguin), the English translation of a novel by Nguyễn Thanh Hiện. She studied at Stanford University.

Ramya Jirasinghe's collection of poems, *There's an Island in the Bone* won the 2011 State Literary Joint Award. She is the author of non-fiction including *Rhythm of the Sea*, *Trinity*, and *When Life Touches Life*. Ramya was long listed for the Fish Poetry Prize, of Ireland, 2011, and was joint runner-up to UK's Guardian-Orange First Words Prize of 2009. Her second poetry collection, *Love Poems from a Frangipani Garden*, was published by the Mica Press, UK, in 2018.

Rina Kikuchi is Professor of Literature at Shiga University, Japan, and Adjunct Associate Professor at the University of Canberra. She is currently working on a research project on Japanese women's poetry of the Asia Pacific War. Her bilingual books of poetry translations include *Poet to Poet: Contemporary Women Poets from Japan* (2017, co-edited with Jen Crawford) and *Pleasant Troubles* (2018, co-translated with Harumi Kawaguchi).

Seb Doubinsky is a bilingual award-winning writer born in Paris. His novels, all set in a dystopian universe revolving around competing cities-states, have been published in the UK and in the USA. He currently lives with his family in Aarhus, Denmark, where he teaches at the university.

Stephen Embleton was born in KwaZulu-Natal, South Africa and is now a resident in Oxford, United Kingdom. His first short story was published in 2015 in the "Imagine Africa 500" speculative fiction anthology, followed by the "Beneath This Skin" 2016 Edition of Aké Review, the debut edition of Enkare Review 2017 and more. He is a charter member of the African Speculative Fiction Society and its Nommo Awards initiative. His debut speculative fiction novel, Soul Searching, published in 2020 was shortlisted for the Ilube Nommo Award in 2021. His unpublished YA fantasy novel, Bones & Runes, was a finalist in the 2021 James Currey Prize for African Literature, and was published in 2022. Stephen is the editor of The James Currey Anthology 2022, featuring short fiction and non-fiction with contributors hailing from Botswana to Nigeria, Ghana to South Africa. Twitter: @spembleton

Sudeep Chatterjee is an Indian writer and translator. Although he primarily writes in Bengali, he is also drawn towards English and Hindi literature, by virtue of being raised in a Hindi speaking area, specifically Varanasi. He is mostly known for his diversity in choosing subjects, stories and concerning areas. His published books dealt with geopolitics, environment and science fiction some of which are dedicated to young adult readers. He is an avid traveler and the travelogue and memoirs written by him are praised by a great deal of people. Sudeep runs an initiative called 'Lore' to spread awareness about dying languages and the literature. He has a passion towards building a world of collaborative work among different cultures & literature styles across the globe.

Tamantha Smith is an English Literature and Creative Writing major, specialising in speculative fiction. She has worked as a journalist and a teacher, and currently works for the Royal Australian Navy. Tamantha is obsessed with classic speculative fiction, but will never turn down a good novella or short story collection. Most of her spare time is spent worrying about the Singularity or wondering if scientists could genetically-engineer a sugar glider-cat hybrid. You can catch her tweeting—often just lurking—@amaranth_au.

Zephyr Li is a classical Chinese poet, educator, poetry curator and a member of British Psychology Society currently based in Wales. His poetry collection is titled *The Soothing Book for Souls* (寧魂集). For translation or teaching enquires, please contact him at zephyrusalavender@gmail.com

We hope you enjoyed Languages of Water. For more exciting anthologies and novels, visit us at www.mvmediaatl.com

CPSIA information can be obtained
at www.ICGtesting.com
Printed in the USA
BVHW050440090623
665619BV00001B/4